Freedom from Depression

6 Keys to Eliminating Emotional Pain

Dr. Tony Piparo

PEAK PERFORMANCE INSTITUTE

(414) 366-0469

Tony@ThePeakSolution.com

www.ThePeakSolution.com

www.FreedomFromDepression.org

Freedom from Depression: 6 Keys to Eliminating Emotional Pain

Paperback
ISBN-10: 0-9769676-7-7
ISBN-13: 978-0-9769676-7-5

Hardcover
ISBN-10: 0-9769676-6-9
ISBN-13: 978-0-9769676-6-8

Electronic
ISBN-10: 0-9769676-4-2
ISBN-13: 978-0-9769676-4-4

First Edition, Second Print
First Printing, June 2017
Second Printing, November 2017

Printed in the United States of American
Freedom from Depression Published By: Peak Performance Institute
5837 S. Quality Avenue
Cudahy, WI 53110 USA

Freedom From Depression has become
an International Best Seller and Amazon #1 New Release.

What People are Saying

"This must-read book provides a clear insight into what depression is all about and how to identify the symptoms in others as well as yourself. This is a life changing read and more importantly a life-saving book. Anthony identifies 6 keys to eliminate emotional pain. I'd say my #1 take away is to share this book with everyone - let's start a movement to 'Change A Life – Save A Life'."

Thomas Ginn
Proctor Gallagher Institute - Thinking Into Results Certified Consultant

"As someone who has attempted suicide, this book contains everything I wish I knew in order to overcome depression, stress, and anxiety very effectively. Improve your mental health with Dr. Piparo's down-to-earth knowledge. 'Freedom From Depression' is a must have for anyone looking to take control of their thoughts and emotions!"

Lucas J. Robak
Authorpreneur Academy – Consultant/Trainer and #1 Bestselling Author

"Dr. Tony Piparo's book creates and provides a window into mental health. Anyone can benefit from the down-to-earth knowledge and strategies shared to overcome depression, stress, and anxiety, as well as a runaway Negative Programming Cycle."

Mary G. Mora
MGM Speakers Bureau - Abundant Talent Connector/Owner

"This book is a basic primer on mental health and depression that should be in everyone's library. In an interesting and easy-to-understand way, Tony thoroughly explains the facts about the causes and devastating effects of depression, including how it has profoundly touched his own life and those close to him. Every chapter has convenient summaries, handy checklists, and step-by-step practices that anyone can easily incorporate into their daily life. I liked that many of the strategies in the book were new to even me, and not the same stuff you see everywhere else."

Debbie Hampton
Authored Beat Depression and Anxiety by Changing Your Brain and Sex, Suicide, and Serotonin

"Anyone who's ever wanted to be able to confidently improve their mental health can benefit from the down-to-earth knowledge in this book."

David Wallace
Principal, Bay Ridge Consulting Group, LLC - Practicing Expert in Business Development and Contributing Author: "Brilliant Breakthroughs for the Small Business Owner"

"Before I knew him, he wasn't good enough. As I got to know him he made me a better golfer. Knowing him made me a better man! And now I love him like a father. Through the highs and lows of life... Tony has been my rock! I honestly don't know where I would be without him! Thanks for everything you've done and continue to do that inspires me to be the best version of myself each day."

Michael Manaley
The Barefoot Broker

"As a how-to guide, this book contains everything you may need to know. Brimming with straightforward strategies anyone can use to overcome depression, stress, and anxiety, as well as a runaway Negative Programming Cycle."

Rev. Maggie Mongan
Brilliant Breakthroughs, Inc. - Master Business Coach & Strategist

"Freedom From Depression is an incredible source of information on depression. I feel like I've taken a 3 credit graduate level course just from reading it. Dr. Piparo gives his personal experiences and family history with depression, along with techniques and strategies to reduce and eliminate the illness.

He has thoroughly researched and integrated his firsthand knowledge with this devastating mental health issue. Piparo, has created an outstanding literary work in terms easily understood by ordinary people. This is a must read for those suffering from depression or provides care for someone who is affected by it."

Heddy Keith
Certified Hypnosis Instructor
Author of Through It All: The Men I Chose To Love and Lessons Learned

WOLFMIND

STRONGER IN THE PACK

Dedication

This book is dedicated to my amazing, talented, and beautiful son who struggled with depression his entire life until he chose to leave his earthly existence on March 16, 2017.

Table of Contents

Acknowledgements

Everyone should be so blessed. I have had the support, encouragement, and access to the wisdom of so many wonderful family and friends throughout my entire life. They have helped me turn hard lessons into experiences for which I am so grateful. They have taken me into their homes at times, always into their lives, and most importantly into their hearts. Without their love and guidance, I would not have reached the point in my life where I rejoice for every experience, good and bad.

It started with my parents. Their parenting style was tough, but their belief in me was so profound that I never gave up and achieved more than I could have hoped. To my grandparents whom I lovingly refer to as Nanny and Papa, I can only say thank you. Nanny displayed so much courage during her glorious 104+ years, given the abuse she suffered as a child. I couldn't imagine going through what she did. A quiet and unassuming matriarch, she possessed the strength of a lion. You were such an inspiration to your entire family. Papa, you died too soon. Your funny quips carried so much wisdom, I wish I had more time with you to learn even more amazing things.

My children, Jennifer Love and T.J. brought purpose and meaning to my life. No matter what I was feeling at the time, just looking into those adorable eyes I understood the meaning of unconditional love. Even as you grew into wonderful adults, I felt your love and presence even when we were far apart.

Dr. Rita Ellithorpe and Matt Oechsli helped me identify and refine my approach to dealing with my own poor self-concept and depression. Even with all my academic success, none of this would have been possible without their insight and wisdom. Thank you for sharing your secrets with me.

Evroula, my beautiful bride, I get down on my knees and thank the stars above for your presence in my life. You bring me so much joy; you use your British sarcasm so I don't take myself so seriously all the time. Don't ever stop.

There are so many people to thank for their help in publishing this book. Lucas Robak, thank you for all the help in formatting the manuscript for publication and setting everything up on Amazon.

I want to pay tribute to Vidal Cisneros for help in teaching me how to prepare myself for the media and promoting the book throughout your vast social network. I am also grateful to Angela Schneider for the incredible cover design. You knew exactly what message I wanted this book to convey and to Heidi Egger for her amazing talent in editing the manuscript.

Michael Manaley, you are such an amazing human being. You picked up the gauntlet when you received the news that my son, your step-brother, died of a self-inflicted wound after suffering through a lifetime of depression. Knowing what you went through as a child and over the last several years, just surviving was more than most people could have accomplished. You possess the heart of a lion and the strength of an oak tree. I cannot even imagine the courage that is necessary to cycle 1,000 miles in 10 days to honor your fallen brother and bring depression and suicide into the light, so no other parent will ever go through what I have.

Finally, I want to thank all the clients who were willing to try a different approach to eliminate stress, anxiety, and depression from their lives. They are more than an inspiration. They are the reason I do what I do.

Introduction

When I first announced my intention to write this book, I was told in no uncertain terms, "The world does not need another self-help book." This was quickly followed by two equally insulting questions, "What does a Sport Psychologist know about depression?" and "Why should people listen to you?" My answers stunned my attacker.

"You are absolutely correct. The world does not need another self-help book, it needs a book that helps. I continued by listing numerous statistics on depression and its many causes and effects. According to the Anxiety and Depression Association of America, the leading cause of disability in the U.S. is Major Depressive Disorder, affecting more than 15 million Americans. Another 3.3 million American adults suffer from Persistent Depressive Disorder or PPD (formerly called dysthymia), a milder form of depression lasting for at least two years.

Depression doesn't occur in a vacuum; it is intimately linked to stress and anxiety, so we must examine the rates of Americans suffering from the many forms of these treatable conditions. Forty million American adults suffer from Anxiety Disorders. Panic disorders affect six million adults. Fifteen million American adults suffer from Social Anxiety Disorder while 19 million adults struggle with specific social phobias. Obsessive-Compulsive Disorder or OCD affects 2.2 million adults and Post-Traumatic Stress Disorder or PTSD affects 7.7 million adults.

Children aren't spared the ravages of stress, anxiety, and depression. According to a 2014 report from the National Institute of Mental Health (NIMH), depression is the most common mental health disorder in the United States among teens with 2.8 million youth age 12-17 experiencing at least one major depressive episode. Between 10% to 15% of teenagers experience some depression at any one time and about five percent suffer from major depression at any given time

As many as 8.3% of teens suffer depression for at least a year at a time, compared to about 5.3% of the general population. Most teens with depression will suffer from more than one episode. Twenty to forty percent experience more than one episode within two years and 70% experience more than one episode. Episodes of teen depression generally last about eight months. About two percent of teens suffer from PPD with 15% eventually developing bipolar disorder.

Medication is the most used method of treatment for stress, anxiety, and depression. According to research published in 2009 in the *Archives of General Psychiatry,* about 1 in 10 Americans takes an antidepressant, now the most commonly prescribed type of drug in the U.S. Much of the surge has happened in the past two decades, increasing from 5.84% to 10.12% in 1996 to 2005 alone. However, a report recently published in *The Journal of the American Medical Association* showed that drugs work best for very severe cases of depression, but produce little to no benefit over placebos (inactive pills) in less serious cases.

Antidepressants also come with potentially dangerous side effects that cause other health problems, the use of even more prescriptive drugs, and a decrease in the quality of life. These include nausea, increased appetite and weight gain, loss of sexual desire and other sexual problems, fatigue and drowsiness, insomnia, blurred vision, constipation, dizziness, agitation, irritability, and rage. Anti-anxiety medications are associated with numerous and equally dangerous side effects, including, cognitive impairment, sleep-driving, sleep-walking, heart problems, amnesia, disruptive behaviors, **depression**, hallucinations, increased risk of suicide, and hostility.

In contrast, Cognitive Behavioral Therapy or CBT, while not associated with dangerous side effects is not always effective. CBT has been shown to be much more effective in treating mild to moderate forms of depression, but far too many individuals remain frozen in their depression. That means there are a large percentage of individuals suffering from depression who are not aided by either medication or CBT. Albert Einstein defined insanity as "doing the same thing over and over again and expecting different results". We need to treat depression, stress, and anxiety differently than we do now if we hope to improve the mental health and quality of life for those individuals not helped by traditional methods.

My attacker was now staring at me in disbelief with her jaw touching the floor, but I continued.

I wanted her to understand what answers a Sport Psychologist might hold and why me. As a Sport Psychologist, I studied what causes talented athletes to disintegrate in the heat of competition to provide them with the assistance they need to perform up to their potential regardless of the demand or pressure to excel.

It all came down to one common factor, fear. The fear of failure becomes so overwhelming that athletes' fight-or-flight reflex is triggered. While this primitive, instinctive, and powerful reflex can save our lives in times of threat, it wreaks havoc on our ability to function in today's modern society, including in sports. Methods for reversing or inhibiting the effects of fight-or-flight had to be simple to understand and put into practice. More importantly, they had to work right here, right now. An athlete cannot wait until later to relax and regroup as there may not be a later. Their performance must improve immediately.

I started with golfers and then adapted my methods for athletes playing other sports. Eventually, I learned that my methods were just as effective in treating business professionals suffering from performance anxiety, students with test anxiety, and everyday people struggling to make it through their fast-paced, hectic, and demanding lives. But would it work for adults and children suffering from depression?

My interest in knowing if I could help others suffering from depression stemmed from the fact that my family had been plagued with depression for generations, starting with my maternal grandmother and including myself. For some, the depression had been so severe and prolonged that it ended in suicide. Sadly, this included my own amazing, talented, and beautiful son.

I don't want children or adults to suffer needlessly when all they need is a little knowledge, support, and access to very simple, yet extremely powerful, scientifically proven methods that clear their minds, calm their nerves, and relax and energize their bodies quickly and easily. I don't want another parent to go through what I did that bleak and tragic day that my son chose to leave his earthly existence behind.

In this book, you will learn what depression is, how it develops, as well as its many causes and effects. You learn about the fight-or-flight reflex and Negative Programming Cycle that are triggered every time stress, anxiety, or depression is experienced. This is important because the human nervous system reacts the same way whether our lives are threatened or our beliefs and expectations about how life should treat us are threatened. Long-term exposure to unresolved stress causes an accumulation of toxic chemicals in the body that compromises your physical and mental health, performance, and quality of life, leading to feelings of helplessness and hopelessness that trigger depression.

Stress, anxiety, and depression need to be addressed and their effects reversed as soon as they are noticed. You can't afford to wait until you can exercise or meditate, two proven strategies that offer relief from these debilitating conditions. Nor do you have the time to wait until you can see your therapist or counselor to work through the latest disaster in your life.

Long-term, you must also learn how to rewire your brain, so that the situations or conditions that led to your mental health issues no longer affect you. Several methods for dealing with an unkind or adversarial world are provided to help improve the functions, structures, and chemistry of your brain to help you improve your beliefs and expectations about yourself and the world in which you live.

Some might consider this a radical approach. I do not. I've seen too many people improve their physical and mental health, as well as their performance and quality of life using these techniques. If you or someone you love is affected by stress, anxiety, and depression and are under a physician's care, please do not stop using any medication prescribed for you. If you haven't already, please seek qualified medical help. Suppressing, repressing, or ignoring mental health issues does not stop them from destroying your life.

My hope is that someday the conditions that led to your mental health issues will subside. Then you and your doctors can decide if you warrant the continued use of medicine or therapy to control your symptoms. I wish you enormous success on your journey back to mental health.

WOLFMIND

STRONGER IN THE PACK

Chapter 1
The Truth About Depression

Before embarking on my journey to develop different options for treating depression and its many causes and effects, I reviewed my family's history with depression relative to the research available at that time, as well as my own experience with this crippling disease. According to the research I could find, depression may be caused by any number of factors, including genetics and biology as well as a variety of social and personal issues that affect one's daily life experiences. These latter two factors include abuse, grief, major life changes, substance abuse, serious illness or injury, medication, and nutrition.

As you will learn, none of these factors predict with 100% accuracy who will develop depression during their lifetime. Rather, depression is a complex mood disorder resulting from the interaction of a combination of many of these factors, as well as some other triggers. It is these other triggers, I believe that offer hope to prevent the onset of depression or to stop it in its tracks early in its development.

Depression: A Family Affair

My passion for understanding depression and developing more effective alternative treatment methods was fueled by my own family's history with this devastating disease. My maternal grandmother was plagued with depression since she was a child and remained with her throughout her glorious 104+ years on the planet. Her depression started when she suffered abuse at the hands of her aunt. Having just gotten divorced, my great grandmother needed to work to support her young family.

Her sister agreed to take care of my grandmother while my great grandmother worked; my grandmother was four at the time. Accusing my grandmother of lying, my great aunt pushed my grandmother's face onto a hot stove, causing third-degree burns on her lips. I'm not sure if the term, Post Traumatic Stress Disorder existed at the time, but I'm sure my grandmother suffered from PTSD from the stories I was told. She developed social phobias that caused her to fear female authority figures, other than her mother, lasting well into her adult years.

If that wasn't bad enough, when she was in her mid-twenties, my grandmother miscarried and had to have a complete hysterectomy. Not being able to conceive another child sent my grandmother into an emotional tailspin that kept her in bed for years. While she never fully recovered, my grandmother was helped through the support of her family, including my mother, an adopted son, grandchildren, great-grandchildren, even great, great grandchildren as well as some mild antidepressants and anti-anxiety medication she referred to as "nerve" pills.

She wasn't the only family member to suffer the effects of depression. Depression also plagued my father's family. His mother, my paternal grandmother, sunk into a depression from which she never recovered when the last of her children left home to start their own families. Medication, Cognitive Behavioral Therapy, and even "shock therapy" never helped. She eventually died from complications of the disease when she was only fifty-four.

My dad's youngest brother, having accepted the role of caregiver for his mother, eventually succumbed to the constant exposure to her condition and was finally diagnosed with Major Depressive Disorder, also known as clinical depression. Uncle Larry was treated with medication for depression, anxiety, and stress his entire adult life. While he improved after several years of treatment, the disease never left him and he sank into fits of depression at various times until he died in his early eighties. While he lived a long time, his quality of life diminished because of his mental illness.

These weren't the only two people in my father's family that suffered from life-long struggles with depression. My Aunt Catherine sunk into a deep depression when her eighteen-year-old daughter suddenly died from a brain aneurism.

To this day, she remains in therapy and is treated with medication to give her some semblance of a normal life.

My parents never seemed too affected by normal fluctuations in every-day life, nor did any of my siblings, but I did. Life treated me well for most of my life, but I fell completely apart when I got divorced and lost a job I loved, both within months of one another. Now in my mid-40's, I went on an emotional roller coaster for several years, finally finding it difficult to function in my day-to-day life and lost the zest to live, including the enthusiasm for things that normally gave meaning to my life and the excitement that got me out of bed in the morning.

Finally, seeking treatment after several years of ignoring and suppressing my stress, anxiety, and developing depression, I resisted when the only thing offered were drugs for depression, high blood pressure, high blood sugar, and high cholesterol caused by co-occurring conditions. The potentially dangerous side effects of those drugs were already known by then. All my doctor told me when I broached the subject of side effects was "Don't worry about it." I wasn't convinced.

Conveying my situation and the treatment plan offered by my physician to my friend Michael, who lived in California, I was relieved when he offered what seemed to be sound advice. He told me to schedule a trip out west so I could get a second opinion from his physician, Dr. Rita Ellithorpe at the Longevity Center in Tustin. Not only was she an MD, she also held a doctorate in Natural Medicine and rarely, if ever, prescribed medication for conditions caused by one's reactions to normal daily life experiences.

The first thing that amazed me was that she scheduled tests my traditional physician never heard of. After the tests were completed, she counseled me for over two hours, explaining the results of my tests and developing a plan to assist in my healing.

She completely altered my diet, prescribed whole food supplements, exercise, and meditation. When I told her what I did for a living, she replied, "Doctor, heal thyself."

A light bulb turned on in my head and I got my first clue about how to treat my depression that became the cornerstone of my journey back to mental health. Not only did I follow her recommendations, I began using the techniques I prescribed my clients to help them overcome the effects of performance anxiety. My experiment was a complete success.

Three months later, I visited my traditional physician. He scheduled the same battery of tests he had prescribed during my original visit. His response to the new results was, "I guess the medications I prescribed for you did their job, because all of your tests came back normal." When I told him that I hadn't taken them and had sought a second opinion from an MD with a degree in Natural Medicine, his only response was, "I was told those things don't work." When I asked him where he got that information, he replied, "pharmaceutical companies".

Six months later my lab results returned consistent with those expected for a healthy twenty-five-year-old. Scratching his head, my doctor could only say, "I guess you need to continue doing what you're doing." I have continued that regimen ever since, especially using my stress-busting methods daily. Now, even the severest test of my sanity, including the death of my son, cannot send my emotional state reeling. Yes, his death hurt me dearly. There are moments when I desperately feel his loss, but I don't descend into that cavern of suffering I once called home.

Only five years prior to my diagnosis, my son was diagnosed with depression, even experiencing suicidal thoughts as a resolution for his emotional pain. How can an eight-year old boy from a good family who loved him dearly and treated him well become so depressed he considered suicide? I was beside myself! So was the rest of the family.

It began when he entered second grade at which time he was diagnosed with learning disabilities. The feeling of being inadequate relative to his classmates eroded his sense of self-worth. While I didn't realize it at the time, his perceptions of my beliefs of his inadequacy also contributed to his poor sense of self. I always tried to convince him that I loved him and just wanted him to be happy. I never thought less of him because of his academic difficulties. However, it didn't register with what he needed to hear.

I guess it was no different for him than it was for me when I was a child. My parents raised me to become the best I could be. Believing that sparing the rod spoils the child, I was spanked when I misbehaved, sometimes rather harshly with a wooden spoon or a strap. This was not considered child abuse at the time, but the norm for how best to raise children.

They also didn't believe in rewarding me for my successes, because I was expected to succeed. The combination of those two parenting patterns, along with a severe childhood illness that was supposed to be my demise before I turned twelve, somehow created a sense of not being good enough to be loved. Feeling inadequate, my reaction was to overachieve. I ended up pursuing four degrees. Even afterward, with all my academic success, I never felt good enough and still was emotionally stunted, feeling pain when I should have experienced great excitement. This realization now allows me to understand the pain my beautiful, talented, and amazing son experienced in his life.

At the time of my son's diagnosis, I was just completing my second master's degree and I had already been accepted by the University of North Carolina at Greensboro to pursue a doctorate in Sport Psychology. His depression worsened as the family moved from Wisconsin to North Carolina. Now he had to interact with a new group of kids who would learn of his disabilities.

Three years later, having completed my doctorate and earned the American Psychological Association's Dissertation of the Year honors only added to my son's insecurities. I didn't know what to do to help him through his depression. I didn't know how to convince him that I did not think less of him because of his learning difficulties. Hell, I didn't know how to convince myself that I was worthy of my father's love and respect.

By the time he was a senior, his condition worsened and one of his counselors found him to be suicidal. The only thing he lacked was a plan. Immediately we got him into therapy that provided some much-needed relief; unfortunately, it wouldn't last. When he turned 19, he was prescribed antidepressants and anti-anxiety medication, but they proved to be no help whatsoever. In fact, they only worsened his depression and intensified his suicidal thoughts and feelings of worthlessness. The mental demons infecting him throughout the day invaded his sleep and he constantly woke drenched in sweat from nightmares that occupied his dreams. Now, he experienced 24 hours of what must have seemed like sheer hell to him.

Even though his battle with depression and poor self-esteem were constant and intense, he managed to thrive, becoming quite gifted in everything he did. He started as a plumber's assistant while still in high school and developed the skill to eventually go into industrial and commercial heating and air conditioning installation. During the last several years of his life, he became a master carpenter and built homes for a living. He also worked for a tree service one summer.

I was always amazed at what he could do and accomplish given the tremendous emotional pain he experienced non-stop. He fought life with every ounce of his being and won. Unfortunately, he just never realized it.

Only work kept his mental demons at bay, so he would take on additional jobs to keep his mind occupied. Until the day he died, he could still take down 100-foot trees, dropping them precisely where he wanted without hitting houses, other trees, or landscaping that were only inches from where the tree needed to fall though he hadn't worked in that industry for nearly a decade and a half.

I could tell you many more amazing things my son accomplished during his 37 years on this planet, but that would take me an entire book. In fact, someday I will write that book, but that is tangent to our present discussion. In the last few weeks before his death, his circumstances changed and dramatically eroded his zest for life. Even though the circumstances surrounding his death call into question whether his suicide was accidental or deliberate, one thing is sure. He was tired of the emotional pain caused by the demons that ate at him constantly.

Hopefully, now you understand why I am so committed, obsessed really, with wanting to help others and their families overcome the devastation depression inflicts. My own family has been plagued with this disease and traditional therapy and treatment offered very little to no help. I just had to believe there was a better way.

Considering my family's four-generational-history of depression, my first inclination was to believe that depression was genetic, passed on from one generation to the next. But wait? Other than my grandmother, there was no history of depression in her immediate family.

My father, nor two of his other siblings ever suffered from depression. My mother, being the only natural child of my maternal grandparents never sank into clinical depression. None of my six natural-born siblings suffered mental health problems. I have two children and my son was the only one who suffered this ailment. My daughter has never been affected by this troubling disease.

Biology and Depression

If genetics determined who will develop depression during their lifetime, you would think that there would be a 100% correlation between depression and family history. Since there was not, at least in my family, I could only see heredity increasing the risk for someone to develop mental health problems. If it's not genetics, maybe biology can predict who will succumb to the ravages of depression and poor mental health.

Research has documented differences in the brains of individuals who suffer from poor mental health when compared to those who do not. It appears that those who suffer from depression have a smaller hippocampus; that tiny part of the brain vital for memory storage that contains structures known as serotonin receptors. These receptors are responsible for the communication across circuits that connect different brain regions involved in processing emotions. A smaller hippocampus means fewer serotonin receptors.

Serotonin is thought to be especially active in constricting smooth muscles, transmitting impulses between nerve cells, and contributing to wellbeing and happiness. Serotonin is thought to be responsible for maintaining mood balance by many researchers; a deficit of serotonin, therefore, would lead to depression. There are also many other regions of the brain implicated in the development of depression, but no single brain structure or pathway fully accounts for poor mental health.

Unless there is a 100% correlation between mental health and specific brain structures, biology, like genetics, can only contribute to the potential for depression, not predict who will develop it during their life. The same research found that individuals with a normally sized hippocampus, while at a smaller risk, may also develop mental health problems; biology cannot be the answer.

Social and Personal Issues Relating to Depression

We must look elsewhere. If it's not genetics or biology, maybe specific life events can predict depression as well as other mental health issues. Abuse, conflict, grief, major life changes, personal problems, serious illness and injury, substance abuse, and diet have all been linked to the development of mental health issues. Again, the relationship between these factors and mental health is not 100% and can only be part of the answer.

Previous physical, sexual, and emotional abuse increases the vulnerability for the development of clinical depression, but cannot predict it. The same is true for individuals witnessing abuse or violence, having a family member devastated by abuse, or caring for someone affected by abuse. Is it any wonder that so many soldiers return from war stricken with PTSD from what they saw and were required to do?

Great sadness or grief from the death or loss of a loved one has been found to increase the risk for depression. The greater the sense of loss, the greater the likelihood for the development of depression and other mental health issues. Again, a great percentage of individuals grieving the death or loss of loved ones never develop clinical depression. Their grief may extend for some time, but their sadness doesn't affect the quality of their life or restrict them from engaging in a normal healthy social life, at least not for very long.

Major changes in one's life, both good and bad, present greater risks for the development of mental health problems. Events considered good, like starting a new job, graduating, or getting married may lead to depression; so can moving, losing a job or income, divorce, or retiring. However, the syndrome of clinical depression is never just a normal response to stressful life events. It's a complete breakdown of the mental and emotional processing of these events.

Another issue associated with a greater risk for developing clinical depression is personal problems. Social isolation from other mental issues, feelings of abandonment, alcoholism, or drug abuse can lead to depression. Again, there is no 100% relationship between personal problems and the development of clinical depression.

Whether it's a change in the chemical make-up of the brain, problems resulting from substance abuse, or the isolation or abandonment that is experienced because of substance abuse, research suggests that 30% of individuals with a substance abuse problem will eventually develop clinical depression. That still leaves 70% with a substance abuse problem who do not.

Sometimes, depression co-exists with severe injury or illness. Fear, whether that fear is related to death, loss of one's quality of life, or life choices, can become so overwhelming that it ends in clinical depression. It is akin to the depression that develops from the sadness or the grief experienced from the death or loss of a loved one.

Treatment Options

After combing the vast amount of research available, I have concluded that depression is an extremely complex disease. No one factor predicts the onset of clinical depression. Genetics and biology, as well as social and personal problems, may all play a role. While depression is a complex disease with no clear predictors of who will develop it during their life, treating depression may be simpler than once thought, at least in the prevention of its onset or the very initial stages of its development.

Research of traditional methods for the treatment of clinical depression, specifically prescriptive medication and Cognitive Behavioral Therapy, offer some relief. Individuals who suffer from significant depression appear to be better served by medication. Unfortunately, medication comes with potentially dangerous, even lethal, side effects. At best, individuals may only develop other health issues that require treatment and additional drugs.

Cognitive Behavioral Therapy appears to work best for individuals who suffer from mild to moderate forms of depression. Unfortunately, CBT and other similar approaches take time to correct an individual's thinking and reaction to aversive life experiences. The process may appear too daunting or the length of time for change to occur too long, so sufferers quit before therapy has a chance to help.

Consequences of Untreated Depression

I know this presents a dilemma for anyone suffering from depression. It was for me. "Should I take prescription drugs, try therapy, or do nothing and hope it goes away." Unfortunately, serious mental health issues, like clinical depression, cannot go untreated. There are too many dire consequences not to seek treatment. According to WebMD, depression takes a serious toll on both mental and physical health. Individuals recovering from a stroke or a heart attack have a tougher time making healthy choices. They also find it difficult following doctors' instructions or coping with the challenges their illness presents and are prone to premature death.

Left untreated, depression may also lead to significant impairment in an individual's ability to function in or enjoy life. The effects of depression range from minor annoyances to death. The most common side effects of depression provide insight into whether a person is suffering from clinical depression and include:

- Poor coping skills

- Anxiety

- Self-medicate with drugs or alcohol

- Decreased immune system functioning

- Sexual dysfunction

- Suicide

- Pain
(headaches and stomach pain)

- Family and marital problems

- Rejection at school or work

- Social isolation

- Self-mutilation

- Premature death

Signs, Symptoms, and Co-occurring Conditions

Depression is classified as a mood disorder that causes persistent feelings of sadness and the loss of interest in normal daily life experiences. It affects how you feel, think, and behave and may lead to a variety of emotional, physical, health, and behavioral problems. You may experience trouble participating in normal day-to-day activities and may feel as if life isn't worth living.

Depression may persist for extended periods undiagnosed as the symptoms an individual experiences may not always be easily identifiable. Those suffering from depression may attempt to ignore, suppress, or hide their condition because of a fear of being judged as flawed psychologically.

Symptoms and signs of depression vary based on age, individual temperament, intensity, and length of time one's life seems out of control. If you or a loved one experience any of the following symptoms, please seek immediate medical attention. This book is to be used as a companion to traditional medical advice.

Mood:

- Daily episodes of depressed mood for extended periods of time (sadness)
- Loss of interest or enjoyment in practically all activities
- The sense of worthlessness or guilt for no apparent reason
- Diminished libido

Physical:

- Loss of energy
- Increased or decreased appetite
- Sleeping pattern changes (increased or decreased sleep)
- Unexplained pain
- Feeling emotionally numb
- Irritability

Behavioral:

- Social withdrawal
- Slowed speech or poverty of speech
- Loss of coordination
- Reduced efficiency for completing tasks

Psychological:

- Hopelessness
- Loss of self-esteem
- Concentration and memory problems (distractibility)
- Trouble making decisions
- Loss of motivation
- Thoughts of suicide or having a plan in place

Co-Occurring Conditions

Depression normally exists with a variety of co-occurring conditions that may be both causes and effects. These co-occurring conditions are also warning signs for the impending development of the disease. If you experience any of these conditions or observe them in others, please seek medical advice.

- Persistent anxiety
- Panic attacks
- Obsessive-Compulsive Disorder or OCD
- Alcoholism
- Substance abuse
- Eating disorders
- Borderline personality disorders

Negative Programming Cycle

After three years of suffering silently from stress and anxiety, I finally sought medical advice as I explained earlier. My reason for seeking medical attention was triggered by an inexplicable weight gain, constant fatigue, poor sleep, and a loss of my normal zest for life. When the doctor provided his diagnosis, I was stunned. I couldn't believe I was suffering from mental illness.

As I began reviewing the occurrences that led to that fateful diagnosis, I realized that my descent into depression began years earlier, probably while I was a child, and quite possibly while I was still in my mother's womb. At the time of my diagnosis, I was only able to trace my depression back to when I first realized my marriage was unraveling. The divorce and loss of the job I loved were just the final straws that broke that proverbial camel's back.

Like most people, I ignored what I was experiencing and focused on what I needed to maintain a semblance of a normal life. And this, from someone whose job it was to help athletes, business professionals, and students overcome the effects of stress and the demand to excel. Not too good there, doctor. Even though I tried to ignore what I was feeling, my thoughts kept drifting to my problems, the consequences of not being able to "fix" those problems, and how I felt because of feeling powerless and inadequate.

I became angry, frustrated, and sad, blaming others for my problems. Surely, someone else was at fault! It couldn't be me. Guilt for allowing others to cause me pain turned into shame. "I should've known better." "I should've taken action sooner." With all my education, training, and success, I couldn't see it coming. I couldn't stop it from happening. Worst of all, I saw no options for making things better.

The more powerless, helpless, and hopeless I felt, the more my anger, frustration, and sadness turned inward and the worse I felt about myself. This was not just a one-time event. It played out from morning to night, day-after-day until I was deep in my own misery. Some might refer to this as a dark night of the soul.

Others would say I experienced a dark night of the ego.

Sometime later I would be introduced to Matt Oechsli, a hypnotherapist and author of such books as *Mind Power for Students* and *Winning the Inner Game of Selling*. He explained that the pattern of internal behaviors I was experiencing was referred to as a Negative Programming Cycle. Negative Programming Cycles affect our beliefs and our beliefs control our thoughts, actions, and emotions.

With each repetition of this pattern, my Negative Programming Cycle strengthened. Finally, it took over my life. I lost my zest for living. As my enjoyment of life vanished, I felt like giving up. Thoughts of suicide played out in my head. If it wasn't for the fact that I had a fear of death, I might have gone through with my plans.

The Negative Programming Cycle consists of a series of connected internal behaviors starting with some triggering event. The triggering event may be related to an unwanted, aversive experience that results in fear. Fear results in threat, triggering a stress response, more commonly known as the fight-or-flight reflex.

The fight-or-flight reflex releases a cascade of hormones intended to save our life when we're physically threatened. Unfortunately, this primitive, instinctive, and powerful reaction to threat wreaks havoc with our participation in normal daily life activities. More about the fight-or-flight reflex and its effects will be presented in the next chapter.

Once in fight-or-flight, our Negative Programming Cycle takes over. Thoughts about the event trigger regret about our past or worry about our future. These thoughts trigger futile attempts to fix our problems and/or our inability to control or improve the situation. As the cycle is repeated over and over, we begin to lose hope, destroying our self-worth. Consistent with these thoughts are the triggering of emotions turned inward furthering disintegrating our belief that we can control the events happening to us and eroding our self-esteem.

Repeated often enough over time, our Negative Programming Cycle results in depression. The speed of one's descent into depression is dependent on several factors, including the intensity of the triggering event, one's level of self-worth at the time of the initial triggering event, genetics, and biology. The typical pattern of Negative Programing Cycles appears on the next page.

Origins of Negative Programming Cycles

Speaking with Matt Oechsli, all of this made complete sense and confirmed what I was doing to treat my condition. It also provided me the impetus to consider developing a plan that would aid in others' recovery from depression and poor mental health. You see, while genetics, biology, and specific life circumstance cannot completely predict who will fall under the shroud of depression, everyone who experiences depression has a well-developed Negative Programming Cycle that undermines their life.

Clearly then, if one intervenes at any point in this downward unraveling of our beliefs, abilities, and self-esteem, the Negative Programming Cycle cannot take over their life. In fact, once the Negative Programming Cycle dies an unceremonious death, an individual is then able to replace it with a powerful Positive Programming Cycle.

This epiphany still left me with two questions burning in my head. The first, "What is the role of the fight-or-flight reflex in the Negative Programming Cycle?" The second, "Why do some people fall victim to Negative Programming Cycles and others do not?" I already knew the answer to the first question as I had helped clients develop the skill to intervene in the fight-or-flight reflex that compromised their performance and participation in their normal daily life activities. I never considered it in the treatment of depression.

What I really wanted to know is what factors create the conditions for Negative Programming Cycles to flourish in otherwise healthy individuals while never catching hold in others? Dr. Shad Helmstetter, author of *What to Say When You Talk to Yourself,* helped me answer that question. According to Dr. Helmstetter, 75%

Negative Programming Cycle

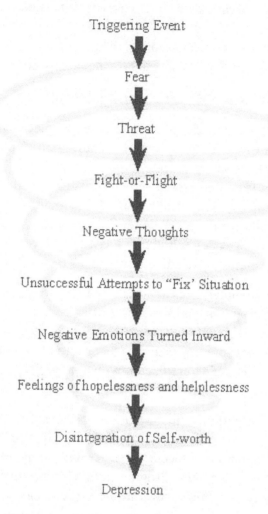

Triggering Event

↓

Fear

↓

Threat

↓

Fight-or-Flight

↓

Negative Thoughts

↓

Unsuccessful Attempts to "Fix' Situation

↓

Negative Emotions Turned Inward

↓

Feelings of hopelessness and helplessness

↓

Disintegration of Self-worth

↓

Depression

of early programming in Western society is typically negative. That is, we tend to be more critical of and punish mistakes more than we reward good behavior and success.

We expect people to make the right choices and behave appropriately, so we don't reward them for positive choices and behaviors. Instead, we criticize and punish them when they make mistakes or make the wrong choices. The greater the discrepancy between positive and negative reinforcement, the stronger the Negative Programming Cycle.

Freedom From Depression

Is it any wonder that we develop the habit of negative self-talk, that we are critical of and even punish ourselves for the simplest mistakes and doubt our ability to improve our performance and choices? You've heard the expression "self-fulfilling prophesy"? Your outward thoughts, words, and behaviors reflect your most deeply held beliefs. If you have a powerful Negative Programming Cycle, you probably respond to adversity the way I did when my marriage fell apart and I lost the job I loved.

But my son wasn't raised through negative reinforcement! He was rewarded for successes and good behavior. I didn't want him to suffer what I went through and yet he did. So why did he develop a Negative Programming Cycle? There are millions of other children who are raised in positive, loving homes where rewards for success and good behavior far outweigh negative reinforcement. While I believe Dr. Helmstetter is correct, there must be a more insidious way that Negative Programming Cycles take hold of a life.

Many years later, my questions would be answered. I came across the works of Dr. Bruce H. Lipton, microbiologist and author of *The Biology of Belief: Unleashing the Power of Consciousness, Matter and Miracles* and neuropsychologist, Rick Hanson, PhD, author of *Hardwiring Happiness: The New Brain Science of Contentment, Calm, and Confidence.* According to Dr. Lipton, genetics is only implicated in 32% of human behaviors, leaving 68% explained by conditioning. Thus, nurture is more important than nature. So it is more likely that we learn to respond to life's challenges in ways that result in the development of Negative Programming Cycles that eventually lead to depression under the right circumstances.

Much of our learning is by deliberate intent, including beliefs, morals, and values as well as such things as language, mathematics, history, computer science, sports, and social skills. However, most things we learn are unintended or accidental. Those responsible for our development don't mean for these behaviors to develop, they just do.

My parents raised me to be a successful and responsible citizen and, for the most part, that's exactly what happened. Unfortunately, in the process, I developed a poor self-esteem, performance anxieties, and social phobias. Fortunately, they weren't that severe and most people didn't know I suffered from these issues. While I was successful and followed the rules, I felt bad about myself and feared being judged.

While my parents never displayed signs of being depressed, they did respond emotionally to stress. Neither of my parents ever finished high school and married at the tender age of nineteen. This limited their earning power early in their married life. Constantly fearing that they wouldn't have enough money to manage their young family, I was constantly exposed to their emotional reactions to financial concerns.

My maternal grandmother was my primary caregiver as both my parents worked to earn enough money to survive, so I was also exposed to my grandmother's depression at a very early age. Consciously I didn't know what was going on, but I could see and feel dysfunctional adult reactions to stress and adversity. Now, my parents and grandmother never intended for me to feel bad or fear judgment, but it was an unintended consequence of how I was brought up and the conditions within which I existed.

I know I never wanted my son to fear social judgment or to develop a poor sense of self. In fact, I thought I was doing everything possible for him to grow up healthy, just like my parents intended for me. Most children who develop a Negative Programming Cycle were brought up by parents who hoped for their future success and happiness.

Fortunately, the effects of early conditioning are not a death sentence if a child develops a Negative Programming Cycle. Even though our brains may be wired with a negativity bias, we possess the ability to overcome any ineffective, inefficient, or defective wiring. This amazing super power is called neuroplasticity. Neuroplasticity is just a fancy term that means we learn and establish new memories through our on-going experiences, encounters, thoughts, emotions, and behaviors. You don't have to understand the science behind neuroplasticity to receive its many benefits or even know how to pronounce it. All you must do is deliberately train your brain in ways that are beneficial.

Neural Structures and Functions

Imagine a telecommunication network that blankets major metropolitan areas like Chicago, Los Angeles, or New York. They're intricate, convoluted spider webs of telephone cables connecting every phone in every building to telephone poles or junction boxes dotting the landscape. Hundreds to thousands of voice, video, and printed messages are sent simultaneously via just one transmission line.

Your brain possesses similar physical structures (neurons, synapses, axons, and dendrites) that function the same way. Every one of your encounters, experiences, thoughts, behaviors, and emotions either initiates the construction of a new telecommunication (neural) network or strengthens the power of existing ones. Neuroplasticity allows you to construct new networks that work for you instead of against you by replacing your old dysfunctional reactions to stress with new deliberate, thoughtful responses that maximize your experiences.

If your fear of failure results in poor testing performance, for example, you have the power to alter your brain's structures, functions, and chemistry to help you test better. You just need the right information, tools, and training. In a very brief time, you become the master of your own internal universe, complete with a new neural telecommunication system that tells you, "you can" instead of "you can't".

How long?

According to Neuropsychologist, Rick Hanson, rewiring the brain is rather simple and only requires about 10 seconds. The way it's done is to focus on positive experiences that energize you. That doesn't sound too difficult, does it? In those 10 seconds, you begin to construct a new neural network that in time causes you to respond to stressful situations in ways that optimize your performance, health, and experience of life.

Since the goal is to automatically respond in stressful situations with beneficial behaviors, it takes more than a single deliberate, conscious response. How much longer? That's up for debate. Automatically responding to stressful experiences in ways that benefit you requires the dismantling of old dysfunctional neural networks while simultaneously constructing new ones. This takes time and consistent application of your new responsive behaviors.

You might have heard about the research of Florida State University professor, K. Anders Ericsson as highlighted in author Malcolm Gladwell's best-selling book, *Outliers: The Story of Success*. According to Ericsson, 10,000 hours of practice were required to achieve international status in such activities as chess, dance, and swimming. I mention this because others reading Gladwell's book or Ericsson's research applied these conclusions to every new behavior or skill. Fortunately, you don't need anywhere near 10,000 hours to develop the power to control your physiology.

Think about how long it took for you to learn other skills. Do you remember what it took to learn to drive a car? If it took 10,000 hours to master this potentially dangerous activity, there would be very few drivers on the road. We'd all be retired before we got our license.

During my Masters and PhD programs, I was taught that skills can be learned in as little as 21 days if the appropriate behaviors are repeated 60 times daily. That means you can optimize your performance, health, and experience of life and replace a Negative Programming Cycle with a Positive Programming Cycle in less than a month. That's not too long, is it?

I now understood why I overcame my depression and other health issues so quickly. It also explained why my clients overcame performance anxiety and struggles with their stressful lives. While I will never know for sure, my strategies may have kept my clients from descending into depression.

They developed the ability to reverse the effects of their fight-or-flight reflex leading to improved performance as well as transform their Negative Programming Cycles into Positive Programming

Cycles. They were now succeeding where they once floundered. They felt good about themselves, so they never remained disappointed over failed performances for very long. Had they not developed these abilities or stronger beliefs in themselves, they may have eventually fallen down that rabbit's hole of depression.

Being exposed to Matt Oechsli, Dr. Ellithorpe, Dr. Shad Helmstetter, Dr. Bruce Lipton, and Dr. Rick Hanson, among others helped me refine and formulate an alternative, or at least, complementary method for the treatment of depression. It includes:

- Understanding how depression develops
- Understanding the effects of fight-or-flight in your daily experiences
- Developing the ability to reverse fight-or-flight quickly and easily
- Replacing Negative Programming Cycles with Positive Programming Cycles
- Establishing healthy lifestyles that include proper sleep, nutrition, exercise, and meditation
- Creating an Action Plan that optimizes the potential for success.

This plan worked for me. It has also worked for numerous clients who have used my methods to improve their performance in sports, business, school, and in everyday life. Many clients already suffering from the initial stages of depression have been able to return to good mental health, some with the additional aid of prescribed medications, others without. Hopefully, after reading this chapter you see a light at the end of a very dark and disturbing tunnel. I wish you well on your journey.

Summary

Depression is defined as a mood disorder that causes persistent feelings of sadness and loss of interest in life. It is caused by a combination of factors including genetics, biology, and unwanted or aversive social and personal problems. It is also characterized by a Negative Programming Cycle and a fight-or-flight reflex that is triggered in times of distress.

While medication has been found to help in severe cases it is also accompanied by potentially dangerous, even lethal, side effects. Therapy has been found to help in mild to moderate forms of depression, but may appear too daunting or take too long to produce the necessary changes. Often sufferers quit before the therapy has had enough time to produce the desired effects.

A complementary or alternative method for the treatment of depression consists of understanding how depression is developed, learning how stress triggers the fight-or-flight reflex during normal daily activities that compromise your life, health, performance, and participation in daily life, the development of strategies that reverse the effects of fight-or-flight and inhibit Negative Programming Cycles from developing or strengthening, as well as changes in lifestyle choices and behaviors. While many other approaches provide relief from depression using one or several of these approaches, none, so far as I know, include a discussion of the effects of fight-or-flight or a step-by-step method for reversing it quickly and easily.

Chapter 2
Stress, Anxiety, Stressors, and Fight-or-Flight

Stress

Long-term exposure to unresolved stress and anxiety activates and strengthens Negative Programming Cycles that, if not abated, result in clinical depression. In this chapter, you will learn what stress and anxiety are, what causes them, and the consequences of not acting to relieve them at the time you're experiencing unwanted, aversive situations. You also learn how stress and anxiety lead to depression, as well as, other physical and mental health issues.

Historical Perspective

Stress, as it is presently used, was originally coined by Hans Selye in 1936. He defined it as a non-specific response by the body to any demand or changing condition, including situations perceived as positive or negative, as both produce the same physiological changes in the body. Selye's theories attracted considerable attention and **stress** soon became the buzzword of the day. Completely ignoring Selye's definition, however, most scientists focused only on reactions to unpleasant, aversive, or unwanted situations. Thus, stress became synonymous with what Selye had defined as **distress**.

According to Selye, any definition of stress must also include reactions to life's pleasurable situations or conditions as they create the same kind of physiological changes as do aversive situations. For this, he used the term **eustress** in which excitement is experienced instead of pain, suffering or distress.

An example of eustress commonly cited is winning a race. It produces the same physiological changes as losing the race, so is just as stressful. Another example is that of a passionate kiss and the resulting contemplation of what might follow. That passionate kiss produces the same physiological changes as do thoughts of painful dental procedures, losing one's house, or failure on a major exam.

Selye struggled unsuccessfully his entire life to find a satisfactory definition of stress, finally redefining stress as "The rate of wear and tear on the body." This is not bad as increased stress accelerates many aspects of the aging process. In his later years, when asked to define stress, he told reporters, "Everyone knows what stress is, but nobody really knows."

All reactions to long-term exposure to unresolved stress, whether the situation producing those responses are determined to be positive or negative, results in the same wear and tear on the body. However, like others of Selye's time, we focus only on situations that result in **distress**. I am sure that the 87% of the people who report higher levels of stress in their lives are describing aversive situations rather than those that might be considered pleasurable and are looking for ways to alleviate the effects of distress, not excitement. If eustress or stress from situations perceived to be desirable affect your health and performance, you can use the same information and strategies identified to address the effects of distress.

Definition: Stress is the mental, physical, and physiological reaction to perceived threats or danger, resulting in fear or concern that important expectations, goals, and dreams are in jeopardy of not being met.

Anxiety

Stress may be experienced without anxiety occurring, but you will never experience anxiety without also being stressed. Stress is just a physiological reaction to threat and occurs unconsciously. This is what happens when your life is threatened. If you worry about a problem, you automatically trigger your fight-or-flight reflex, so you experience the potential threat physiologically.

This is commonly referred to as **psychosocial** or **psychobiological** stress because it relates to **perceptions** of threat in social settings and the resulting **physiological** changes created by those perceptions. The more important your expectations, goals, and dreams and the more you fear them not being realized, the greater your experience of stress.

Stressors

Sources of modern-day stress are all around us and include both external and internal events. External sources include aversive situations related to work, school, relationships, time constraints, media overload, illness, and environmental conditions, such as elevated sound levels, over-illumination, overcrowding, and pollution. Internal sources include dehydration, poor nutrition, and chemical ingestion of drugs and alcohol as well as thoughts related to any external situation perceived to threaten one's hopes, dreams, or expectations for how life should be and/or the consequences of those threats.

Thinking or worrying about unwanted, unpleasant, or aversive situations is just as stressful as experiencing them. That's because the subconscious mind doesn't know the difference between what is real and what is vividly imagined. This is the reason we become frightened while watching a scary movie. Your conscious mind recognizes that what is happening in the movie or on the TV screen is acting, but your subconscious responds as if it's real.

Imagine you are watching a movie where an actress portrays a young woman walking alone on a darkened street. A short distance away, a serial killer with a very large, very sharp knife hides in the bushes waiting for her to get close enough to carry out his evil deed. As you watch the scene unfold the hair stands up on your neck, you bite your nails and close your eyes. You feel tension in the pit of your stomach. Your body begins to shrink into your chair. Suddenly, he leaps out of the bushes, grabs her around the waist, pulls her close to his body, and cuts her throat from ear to ear.

When the actor jumped out of the bushes you may have jumped in your chair, tightened your grip on the armrests, or screamed. When the poor woman's limp body fell to the ground you may have felt sorry for her or anger towards the perpetrator of the crime. It didn't really happen, but you responded as if you were walking down the same street as our young victim, watching every gory detail of the attack, instead of the portrayal of an imaginary crime.

Losing one's home to foreclosure, failing to meet important deadlines at work, or major exams at school are frightening and stressful experiences. Thinking about or fearing stressful experiences and their dire consequences alters your physiology. It's as if you were reliving the aversive situation.

If you experience any or all these events, you are being stressed both by the experience and your thoughts and fears of their dire consequences. The more often you think or worry about stressful situations or their negative consequences, the more often you stress yourself out. The more intense the situation is experienced or perceived and the more negative the consequences, the more stress you experience, producing even greater effects on your performance, health, productivity, and quality of life.

The term **stressor** is thus used to describe situations that result in physiological changes in the body because of the release of stress hormones, whether the situation is perceived positive or negative. Again, here we limit our discussion to those situations perceived to be distressing. The word perceived is used because not everyone responds precisely the same way to a given situation. For example, most people don't like driving in bumper-to-bumper traffic and find this situation stressful, some to the point of rage. Others remain unaffected and use the time to meditate, clear their head, or just enjoy the solitude.

For most people, losing one's job is quite stressful as is the potential loss of income and the impact this may have on them and their family. Some people hate their jobs and may be relieved when they get laid off or fired. Still, others might become exhilarated by potential opportunities that await them because they are no longer chained to a job they may not have liked in the first place. It all depends on your personality, conditioning, history, experience, and beliefs or perceptions, and whether you feel your life or circumstances are beyond your control.

Fight-or-Flight

Thousands of years ago our human ancestors were endowed with, developed, or were programmed as part of some sort of Intelligent Design (depending on your beliefs) with the capacity to respond to potential threats to help them survive their hostile environment. This powerful, instinctive, and primitive reflex is known as **fight-or-flight**. The fight-or-flight reflex is one activity carried out by the Sympathetic Nervous System (SNS) which is one of two subsystems of the Autonomic Nervous System (ANS). The other subsystem is scientifically known as the Parasympathetic Nervous System (PNS) or colloquially as "rest-and-digest". This is our normal state of being; it is the only state where the body is capable of healing itself.

The Autonomic Nervous System is a control system that acts largely unconsciously and regulates heart rate, respiration, papillary response, urination, and sexual arousal. The Sympathetic Nervous System's main function is the activation of the fight-or-flight reflex in times of threat. The main function of the Parasympathetic Nervous System is to activate the rest-and-digest response and return the body to homeostasis once the fight-or-flight response has done its job.

Effects of fight-or-flight

The fight-or-flight reflex releases powerful neurotransmitters or hormones into the bloodstream, including epinephrine (adrenaline), nor-epinephrine (nor-adrenaline), cortisol, and aldosterone. The combined physiological changes resulting from these chemicals are designed to alert you to the potential for danger and prepare you to respond to that threat by boosting your energy to flee or stay and fight, whichever results in the greatest potential for your survival.

The pupils in your eyes dilate. Your eyes are kept in constant motion searching the horizon for the source of the threat. Your peripheral vision widens. Your senses of smell and hearing are heightened. Together these behavioral changes help you identify the source of the threat quickly. Your blood pressure increases to provide more oxygen, thus more energy, to your extremities, so you respond with greater speed and strength. These occur instinctually. You don't have to think about them. You just react, thanks to your fight-or-flight reflex

In addition to activating your survival instincts, your Sympathetic Nervous System simultaneously suppresses those systems not involved in your survival, as the continued activation of these systems impedes your reaction to the impending threat. Reacting too slowly could mean your demise. This includes suppression of your immune, digestive, and reproductive systems.

It also severs the connection between the left and right hemispheres of the brain. The left hemisphere is used primarily for skills requiring higher brain functioning and logical thinking. The right hemisphere is used primarily for emotions or feelings. Access to memories and higher cognitive functions not involved in your survival are also suppressed or shut down.

Consequences of Exposure to Stressful Situations

Because the human nervous system has not changed or evolved since the time our earliest ancestors walked the Earth, all threats are treated the same, whether that threat is to our lives or to our expectations, hopes, and dreams of how we think life should be. Thus, modern day stresses are treated no differently than primitive threats to human survival. Unfortunately, stress hormones don't naturally dissipate from the body.

The presence of these chemicals produces deleterious effects on your performance, behavior, emotions, attention, and mental clarity in the moment as well as long-term. The motivation to engage in any of life's activities wanes as you feel helpless and hopeless to control the situations that you perceive important and uncertain. Waning or complete lack of motivation leads to all sorts of inappropriate or destructive behaviors finally leading to **depression**.

Short-term Consequences

The effects of stress on all mental and physical tasks can range from mild to severe, possibly starting out small or even going unnoticed. You make a mistake, forget a name or phone number, or where you left your car keys. Then you start thinking about making other mistakes or the consequences of making mistakes and failure, distracting you from the task at hand. Becoming frustrated, angry, or sad increases your stress until you're in a full-blown state of panic.

Now stress hormones flood your body. Your brain is in overdrive. Thoughts race through your mind like a hamster on an exercise wheel. You try to block out the stress to no avail. Later, when the incident is well over, your nervous system begins to return to normal. Everything you forgot, you remember and everything you couldn't figure out is now as plain as the nose on your face. Once again you can perform mental and physical tasks the way you are capable and can't believe or understand why you couldn't do it before.

Visual Impairment. One of the first things that happen when stress strikes is a change in vision. Pupils dilate to increase peripheral vision. Your eyes move wildly from side to side. These visual changes helped our ancestors quickly locate the source of danger. Even though you may not be aware of these changes, they wreak havoc on your ability to perform physical and mental tasks in today's modern world. As your peripheral vision widens, your brain must process more information, most of which enters your mind unconsciously.

With your eyes in constant motion, it's difficult to focus on a single point in space or control eye movement. Archers, marksmen, and free throw shooters in basketball all would find it difficult to hit their targets. Reading becomes more difficult, so do tasks that require fine attention to detail.

Pitchers in baseball need to keep their eyes and attention fixated on the catcher's mitt if they hope to throw strikes. Students need to be able to see and focus their eyes on the page in front of them when studying or taking tests if they hope to learn or answer questions correctly. Think of various aspects of your life. How would blurred vision, constant changing visual focus, or an inability to focus on the task at hand affect you?

One consequence of stress our ancestors probably rarely experienced was tunnel vision, at least those that survived. Some animals experience this phenomenon; that's why the phrase, "a deer in headlights" has become part of the language. A quarterback in football needs fluid visual awareness of the entire playing field, especially as he retreats from the line of scrimmage while passing.

If he becomes a deer in the headlights visually focused on only one defender bearing down on him, he might not feel the onrush of others resulting in a sack, possibly fumbling the ball in the process. Or he might fixate on only one receiver who happens to be well-guarded. This could result in a blocked pass or worse yet, an interception. When driving, operators of motor vehicles need to be able to see both ahead and behind them to minimize the chances of getting into an accident.

Sensory Distractions. Increased auditory or olfactory awareness may save your life when you're physically threatened, but interferes with your ability to focus on the task at hand. For example, you're at work, feverishly trying to meet a fast-approaching deadline for a crucial assignment. Because you fear the consequences of not completing the deadline, you stress out. Your heightened sense of smell causes you to become acutely aware of perfume or cologne worn by one of your coworkers. Normally you don't smell it. Because you're so stressed, you're more sensitive to odors and can't get that smell out of your mind and it drives you nuts.

You're taking a final exam at school and you come across a question that you don't readily know the answer. You wrack your brain to figure out the problem or remember the information. You begin to fear failing the exam or at least not doing as well as you expected. In your panic, you notice another student tapping the desk with his/her fingers. The sound is so irritating, you can't keep your mind focused.

Muscular Inconsistencies. Increased energy is directed to muscles in your arms and legs providing you with greater strength and speed. This is very helpful if you are running from some hungry predator looking for its next meal or soldiers engaged in hand-to-hand combat. However, it is destructive for tasks that require fine-motor control.

The increased adrenaline produces tense, jittery muscles. Stressed-out tennis players' legs may feel heavy and find it difficult to move from side to side or from the front of the court to the back, hampering their ability to get to the ball. Hitters in baseball might experience a loss of control of their bat and swing wildly at pitches. Infielders may cleanly field sharply hit ground balls only to throw wildly to first base. Golfers may find their swing gets faster and shorter seriously destroying the precision and near-perfect timing necessary to hit the ball where they had intended

Decreased Memory and Loss of Higher Brain Functioning. You don't need to remember a list of facts or how to solve algebraic equations when running or fighting for your life. In its infinite wisdom, the human nervous system suppresses activities that require memory or complex thinking, maximizing your chances of survival when your life is threatened. Unfortunately, higher brain function and memory are suppressed when you're under a great deal of pressure.

Any activity that requires access to information stored in memory or problem solving where analysis and synthesis of data, deductive and inductive reasoning, interpretation, and inference are required is affected when you're unduly stressed. The more intense the situation, the more your cognitive functioning is affected.

Loss of Emotional and Behavioral Control. A bundle of nerves called the corpus callosum connects right and left hemispheres of the brain, allowing communication between them. Stress severs this connection, interfering with your decision-making processes. You might make the wrong choice or, if you're severely stressed, find that you experience great difficulty controlling your emotions and behaviors.

This may result in rage or physical attacks of coworkers, family, friends, and strangers. This is not to excuse unacceptable behaviors or extreme expressions of emotion, but merely to explain them. Individuals who lose control of their thoughts, emotions, and behaviors don't need a lobotomy. They need to understand how to control their physiology.

Long-term Consequences of Exposure to Unresolved Stress

As far as we know, our early ancestors didn't experience prolonged unresolved stress. Their lives were threatened periodically, but once the threat was survived, they returned to their normal state. They didn't obsess or complain about how hard their lives were. Today, we rarely experience threats to our lives, yet we are constantly in a state of fight-or-flight. We experience threats to how we want to experience life and then obsess and constantly complain about our bad luck or hard lives.

For many, this constant battle with unfriendly circumstances results in a state of hypertension with their nervous system in constant fight-or-flight mode. During fight-or-flight, your blood pressure elevates and your immune, digestive, and reproductive systems are suppressed. Long-term elevation in blood pressure and suppression of your immune, digestive, and reproductive systems results in numerous health problems.

Hypertension or Chronic High Blood Pressure. High blood pressure experienced during prolonged periods causes arteries to narrow, thicken, and harden with fatty deposits called plaque. This process is referred to as arteriosclerosis and dramatically reduces the amount of oxygen-rich blood available to nourish your heart, brain, and other tissues. The build-up of plaque increases the risk of stroke and a variety of heart-related problems, such as a heart attack or congestive heart failure

High blood pressure damages blood vessels throughout the body and reduces the kidneys' ability to remove waste and excess fluid from the body. Continued accumulation of body fluids, in turn, increases blood pressure continuing a never-ending vicious cycle. Other devastating effects of chronic high blood pressure include diabetes, vision problems, memory loss, fluid build-up in the lungs, angina, and peripheral artery disorders.

Immune Suppression. Prolonged stress results in chronic suppression of the immune system, affecting the body's ability to fight off infection and disease. A study reported in the New England Journal of Medicine found that people under continuous stress were more likely to get colds. David Spiegel, MD, psychiatrist and researcher at Stanford University stated that stress adversely affects components of the immune system involved in fighting off diseases like cancer.

Overproduction of an immune factor known as IL-6 is associated with such age-related issues as cardiovascular disease, osteoporosis, arthritis, type-2 diabetes and mental decline. It has also been found that stress acts through the immune system to create inflammation in the body. Inflammation has been linked to body and joint aches and pains as well as allergies and food sensitivities.

Digestive Distress. According to Dr. Kenneth L. Koch, professor of gastroenterology and medical director of Gastroenterology at Wake Forest School of Medicine in Winston-Salem, North Carolina, stress effects every part of the digestive system. Digestion shuts down because the central nervous system suppresses blood flow, affects contractions of the digestive muscles, and decreases secretions needed to metabolize food. Stress has been linked to inflammation of the gastrointestinal system, making you more susceptible to a variety of disorders.

Many people scoff at the idea that stress is the root of digestive problems as it sounds like science is blaming victims. However, Robert M. Sapolsky, a Stanford University stress expert and author of *Why Zebras Don't Get Ulcers,* answers these protests by stating that in times of threat, our bodies are designed to focus on things that help us survive. When our ancestors had to run away from man-eating predators, they didn't need to waste energy on less important things like proper digestion.

A highway of nerves runs directly from your brain to your digestive system with information flowing in both directions. Ninety-five percent of the body's serotonin, a hormone that controls mood, is found in the digestive system, not the brain. So when the brain feels stressed, it unleashes a cascade of hormones that are sent directly to the digestive system, sending it into an uproar. In the short term, stress causes stomach aches, nausea, and diarrhea. Chronic stress creates or aggravates such digestive-related diseases as irritable bowel syndrome, indigestion, heartburn, ulcers, ulcerative colitis, and Crohn's disease. The last two, known together as inflammatory bowel disease, may not be directly caused by chronic stress, but are worsened by it.

Sleep Deprivation is both a cause of and byproduct of prolonged exposure to unresolved stress. In the short term, sufferers experience performance decrements, memory loss and cognitive impairment, an inability to participate in certain daily activities that require sustained attention, increased risk of injury, and automotive accidents. Long-term sleep disorders include high blood pressure, heart attack, heart failure, stroke, obesity, psychiatric problems, including **depression** and other mood disorders, Attention Deficit Disorder (ADD), mental impairment, as well as fetal and childhood growth retardation.

Reproductive Disorders. Watch any sporting event on television and you will be bombarded with advertising directed at any one of several medications designed to assist men suffering from Erectile Dysfunction (ED). When our early male ancestors' lives were threatened, their nervous systems suppressed their ability to become sexually aroused. Sex would be the last thing someone would think about when in fight or flight.

Unfortunately, sexual arousal is suppressed when modern stresses strike. Prolonged exposure to unresolved stress completely shuts down the body's ability to engage in sex. Is it any wonder, the airwaves are filled with advertising for ED solutions?

Women aren't immune either. Sexually active women whose husbands or male partners are affected by ED can become sad, frustrated, and depressed because of the reduction in their quality of life. Stress also affects a woman's desire for sex, leaving her husband or male partner frustrated. Stress has been linked to more severe symptoms of PMS. Couples, looking to start or expand their families where one or both experience long-term stress, are finding it difficult to get pregnant.

Psychological, Emotional, and Behavioral Disorders. In addition to the physical side effects of stress, feelings of hopelessness and helplessness lead to a loss of motivation and enjoyment of life. Depression and anxiety set in, as do other mood disorders. Prescriptive medications don't cure depression and anxiety, they only suppress their symptoms. It's no different than taking medication for a cold.

Medication doesn't cure colds, it hides their symptoms; you're still sick. You just don't know it until the medication wears off. Then you need to take more drugs until your body naturally fights off the cold. When taking medication for stress, depression, anxiety, and other mood disorders, your symptoms may be suppressed until the medications wear off. Unfortunately, unless you do something to address the source of the stress, your conditions remain.

This could last for the rest of your life. For many, turning to drugs, alcohol, or other inappropriate behaviors seems like the only course of action to help them stop obsessing about their problems or keep the demons in their head at bay. Below, find a complete list of all the chronic diseases and conditions related to stress and anxiety.

Consequences

In addition to performance disruption, **long-term** unresolved test anxiety, performance anxiety, or any other form of stress produces severe cognitive, emotional, behavioral, and health issues, including:

- high cholesterol & blood pressure
- diabetes
- heart disease
- susceptibility to infections
- stroke
- immune system disorders
- acid reflux disease
- cancer

- peptic ulcers
- inflammatory bowel disease (IBD)
- sleep disorders (nightmares)
- chronic pain, especially in the back, neck, head, and shoulders
- ADD/ADHD
- tension and sinus headaches (migraines)
- diminished sexual desire
- more severe PMS in women
- panic attacks
- anxiety (test & performance anxiety)
- emotional problems (PTSD)
- rage
- chronic fatigue
- fibromyalgia
- flashbacks
- excessive fear (stage fright)
- depression (prolonged sadness)
- unexplained weight gain or loss

Stress has also been linked to allergies, asthma, skin disorders, unexplained hair loss, and periodontal disease. Even alcoholism and drug abuse can be linked to prolonged, consistent exposure to stress. In fact, research now suggests that almost every major illness people acquire is linked to chronic stress (Segerstrom and Miller, 2004; Kopp and Réthelyi, 2004; McEwen and Lasky, 2002; McEwen and Seeman, 1999). Primary care physicians cite stress as a major contributing factor in 75-90% of their patients' visits.

So what should we do? Is the only answer resigning ourselves to less than we deserve because of living in a fast-paced, hectic, and demanding world? Should we take prescriptive medications for the rest of our lives to deal with anxiety and depression as well as medications for all the side effects caused by these drugs? Should we self-medicate with drugs or alcohol? Should we resort to rage, violence, and aggression to resolve conflict? Americans spend more on healthcare than any other country yet we're ranked 37th in health. Is there anything we can do to improve this very bleak picture? The answer is a definitive and resounding yes!

Assignment

Do you experience any of the health-related illnesses associated with stress? Do you experience mental, emotional, or psychological issues associated with stress? Is your performance in sports, business, school, or life in general affected by stress? Is your experience of life affected by stress? Please review the sections describing the long- and short-term problems associated with stress and anxiety, listing any you are experiencing.

_____

_____

_____

_____

_____

_____

_____

_____

_____

_____

_____

_____

_____

_____

Summary

- Stress and anxiety are both normal experiences of living in a fast-paced, hectic, and demanding world that threaten our hopes, dreams, and expectations for how we want life to t reat us.
- Threats, whether to our life or perceptions of how life is treating us, trigger fight-or-flight.
- Reacting to threats to our life this way is natural.
- Reacting to our perceptions of life this way is not. It is a learned behavior.
- While the activation of the fight-or-flight reflex may save our lives in times of physical threat, it wreaks havoc on our ability to function in modern day society.
- Long-term unresolved stress and anxiety trigger Negative Programming Cycles that, if left unabated, lead to a loss of self-esteem, feelings of hopelessness and helplessness, and a loss of motivation to engage in life, finally spiraling down into depression.

You may not be able to do anything to alter what you experience in life but you can control how you respond to what you experience. All it takes is an awareness of when you're stressed and anxious, a willingness to change, and access to methods designed to reverse or inhibit the destructive effects of runaway fight-or-flight. In the next chapter, you will be exposed to a very simple, yet extremely powerful, scientifically-proven method that accomplishes all three of those things quickly and easily. It is referred to as the Stress and Anxiety De-Activation Routine or SADAR.

Chapter 3
Strategies for Immediate Relief of Stress and Anxiety

Stress is a physiological reaction to a threat, triggering changes in behaviors, thoughts, and emotions. Stress can be related to threats to your life or any situation that is deemed important and the outcome uncertain. Your body reacts instinctively to stress without you even thinking or worrying about a problem. The more important and uncertain the outcome the more stress you'll experience.

Anxiety is the cognitive component of stress. That is, you worry about what you perceive to threaten you, your life, or your performance. You may experience stress without worry; you cannot experience anxiety without getting stressed. Anytime you worry about a problem, your body automatically reacts as if your life was threatened. In other words, worry triggers your stress response, more commonly known as fight-or-flight.

When your body goes into **fight-or-flight**, you become the 'victim' of your own chemistry. Over time, the more stress you experience and the more intense your experiences, the more you begin to identify with that label. You "victimize" yourself every time you think, worry, or tell others about your hard life, poor luck, or the uncaring world in which you live. This reinforces the belief that you are a victim. You start to expect your hard life, poor luck, or mediocre performance to continue. You feel justified in your role as a victim and society's many institutions reinforce this belief.

This process is referred to as a Negative Programming Cycle. Over time, unresolved stress, anxiety, and a run-away Negative Programming Cycle result in a loss of self-esteem, feelings of hopelessness and helplessness, and loss of motivation, eventually leading to depression. With the proper information and training, both fight-or-flight and Negative Programming Cycles are stopped in their tracks.

There are numerous simple tools and techniques for reversing the effects of fight-or-flight and runaway Negative Programming Cycles. When you bundle these techniques together into a simple comprehensive routine, you quiet your mind, calm your nerves, and relax your body. You also reactivate the memories and higher brain functions necessary to succeed as well as systems necessary for a healthy, productive life. This routine is referred to as the Stress and Anxiety De-Activation Routine (SADAR).

SADAR improves your chances for success and happiness by stopping additional stress hormones from entering your bloodstream and purging your body of stress hormones released at that moment. It also floods your bloodstream with endorphins – feel good hormones – to balance your nervous system. Additional steps can be added to the basic routine to further improve your memory, vision, focus, and cognitive functioning. Your brain is now working at peak performance left-to-right and top-to-bottom and is referred to as whole-brain functioning.

The Stress and Anxiety De-Activation Routine (SADAR)

SADAR consists of several steps. Before using SADAR, please read through each step to familiarize yourself with how each are performed. A few steps require minimal training before they do the work for which they are intended.

1. Stop

2. Close your eyes (unless you're operating an automobile or other dangerous equipment)

3. Transform your breathing

4. Relax your body

5. Smile

6. Change your energy

7. Quiet your eyes

SADAR requires anywhere from 30 seconds to five minutes to complete. The more skilled you are, the faster it works and the less time is required to produce positive effects. Initially, expect to spend about five minutes training the routine into your subconscious. You will be practicing in stressful and non-stressful situations. Once learned, you will use it to reduce fight-or-flight effects any time you get stressed or realize you're worrying.

You will notice the greatest effect in stressful situations. Even though the effects may be negligible in non-stressful situations, the routine reduces stress hormones that accumulated over time. Stress hormones build up because they don't dissipate naturally. They must be deliberately flushed from your body. Since we continually stress out or worry about things going on in our life, we're constantly accumulating additional stress hormones. Using SADAR when you're not stressed or anxious removes hormones that have previously accumulated.

Practice

It is highly recommended that you practice when you wake up and just before going to sleep. It is also recommended that you practice as many times during the day as you can. Many of my clients practice for 1-2 minutes at least 10-20 times a day. Some of my clients practice quite a lot more, especially those who come from the fields of sports, business, or academia where split-second changes in thoughts and emotions are the difference between success and failure.

They report that in the time it takes to slowly close and open their eyes, they change their breathing pattern, reduce unnecessary tension, elevate their mood, and improve their thought control. If you want to produce these dramatic changes, you must remain committed to using the routine 20-30 time per day for at least three months. Doing so will prevent your descent into or recovery from depression.

Even after the preliminary training period, it's necessary to continue practicing on a more limited basis (once or twice a week).

You know the old saying, "use it or lose it". That way, you automatically use it when you get stressed or anxious. You won't have to think about using it, you just will.

One effective way to help you learn and remain committed to the process is to involve others. You can teach these techniques to your parents, siblings, other relatives, friends, or anyone who is willing to learn. As these techniques work in any stressful environment, they are beneficial for everyone to learn.

Step 1: Stop

Reactions to stress are so ingrained, so automatic, so instinctive that most people react before they think about what they're doing. Even people who desire to replace dysfunctional reactions with beneficial responses don't remember to use SADAR until much later, at least at first. That's okay. SADAR works every time you use it, even if you're not stressed out at the time.

Initially, you need something to remind you to practice or to use when your dysfunctional reactions to stress kick in. Science has shown that vivid images are easier to remember than words and vivid images combined with words are even more powerful. Red has also been shown to grab one's attention more so than other colors.

On a trip to the Findhorn Foundation Community Gardens and College in Scotland, I observed a stop sign that read "Stop Worrying" on one of their street corners. I found this to be a powerful image and I have used it ever since to help my clients remember to practice. It incorporates everything science says is required to attract your attention. Make copies of the illustration, color the stop signs with a red magic marker, and place them everywhere you will notice, like next to your bed, on your bathroom mirror, in the car, your locker at school, or desk at work. Can you think of any other places you could keep them?

Step 2: Close your eyes

Seventy-five percent of what we respond to daily is visual in nature. Your vision is divided into two subsystems, **central or focusing vision** and **peripheral vision**. Each is connected to a different part of the brain. Central or focusing vision is connected to the cerebral cortex or thinking brain and accounts for only one percent of your total visual field. Central vision is used for activities like reading, targeting, or directing your attention to specific details.

Peripheral vision is part of the Sympathetic Nervous System, so it stimulates the brain unconsciously. You are not consciously aware of what you see peripherally, accounting for 99% of the total visual field. Even though you're not conscious of most of what you see your brain still processes that information. The more stressed you are, the wider your peripheral vision and the more information your brain is forced to process.

Closing your eyes constricts your pupils and stops your eyes from moving like a tuning fork. Your peripheral vision returns to normal. Since your mind no longer focuses on visual stimuli, the amount of information your brain processes is reduced, making it much easier to focus.

Step 3: Transformational Breathing

Breathing is life. We can exist for weeks without food, days without water, but only minutes without breathing. Your body contains 75 trillion cells providing the energy needed to carry out every brain and organ function and body movement. Cells need two things to produce energy – nutrients (food) and oxygen. Cell (oxygen) starvation results in numerous problems, including anxiety and stress, confusion, fatigue, **depression**, loss of focus, and physical performance disturbances. Researchers have concluded that we age, mainly because of an insufficient supply of oxygen to the brain.

The brain, like all organs, requires a continuous and abundant supply of oxygen. Although it represents approximately three percent of our total body mass, the brain requires 20% of available oxygen. Even a slight reduction in the amount of oxygen the brain receives produces disastrous effects.

An oxygen-efficient body is the secret to health, longevity, and peak performance. The most oxygen-efficient exercise available is proper breathing. Improved oxygen supplies have been found to cure diseases and helps you avoid additional diseases and conditions while aiding your physical and emotional balance.

Breathing and State of Mind

The way we breathe is inseparable from our state of consciousness. That is, the way we breathe affects our state of mind and, conversely, our state of mind affects the way we breathe. Under normal circumstances, the average person takes about 15 breaths per minute. Stress, anxiety, mental agitation or overload, and a hectic lifestyle increase the rate of breathing. It becomes faster and shallower. Sometimes you might even hold your breath.

Rapid, shallow breathing provides less oxygen to your brain, making it difficult to process information. Mental clarity, sensory awareness, and the ability to control your thoughts and emotions are diminished. Individuals who lead fast-paced, hectic lives tend to breathe rapidly all the time. They become so acclimated to this lifestyle, they aren't aware of their dysfunctional breathing.

When you breathe slowly, deeply, and rhythmically, you think more clearly and are more likely to be in an 'Awakened' or 'High-Performance' state of mind or what Mihaly Csikszentmihalyi, Professor of Psychology at the University of Chicago refers to as 'Flow' or 'The Zone.' Breath control is such a powerful technique it is the cornerstone of many Eastern philosophies and disciplines like yoga, t'ai chi ch'uan, and karate.

Breathing Patterns

Watch a baby breathe, especially when it sleeps: that little belly continues to rise and fall in perfect rhythm. The child is completely relaxed, so he or she gets much-needed rest. This breathing pattern creates greater relaxation. Being relaxed sends more oxygen to your body and brain, boosting your confidence, providing you with clarity of mind and facilitating your performance or experience of life.

Belly or reverse diaphragmatic breathing is the way we were designed to breathe, filling our lungs completely and allowing oxygen to travel throughout our body. Somewhere in early adolescence, our breathing pattern changes. We hold in our stomachs and breathe completely from our chests, allowing very little oxygen to travel to the rest of our body. You need as much oxygen as possible flowing through your respiratory system to remove stress-induced impurities and other toxins from your body.

Infant style belly breathing is the best way to accomplish this. Changing your breathing pattern is easy, but it takes time and practice. Transformational Breathing, which is what we call deliberate, slow, deep, breathing if practiced daily for about a month, makes belly breathing your dominant pattern. This type of breathing has been found to remove up to 90% of stress hormones recently released into the body or a small percentage of those hormones that have accumulated over time.

Don't worry if you can't belly breathe right away. The goal is to breathe as slowly and as deeply as possible, especially in stressful situations. Even if you never convert to reverse diaphragmatic breathing, you will still benefit if your breathing remains slow and deep. Please read the complete set of instructions before practicing it.

Benefits

Transformational Breathing flushes out most of the stress hormones circulating in your body as well as some that have accumulated over time. In doing so, the tension your body holds is released. It slows down your thinking, allowing you to organize your thoughts into a coherent pattern and keeps you from maladaptive thoughts of doom and gloom. It also improves your memory and access to those higher brain functions necessary to succeed.

Assignment

- Close your eyes.
- Inhale **slowly** and **deeply** through your nose to the count of four.
- When done properly, your abdomen expands first, followed by your chest and upper back, in that order. At no time do your chest, back, and shoulders rise upwards towards your ears. They only expand outwards.
- Hold your breath for two seconds.
- Exhale through your mouth to the count of eight. When done properly, air is first expelled from your upper back, then your chest, and finally your abdomen.
- Hold your breath for one second and then repeat the process from start to finish.

Spend the next five minutes practicing this very slow, very deep form of breathing. Then practice breathing slowly and deeply a minimum of 5-10 times per day for a minimum of 2-5 minutes each time. Expect a complete reversal of your breathing pattern in a few short weeks. You'll greatly reduce tension and stress in your body and will respond much better whenever you get stressed or anxious. Breathe this way alone, in combination with any of the other techniques of SADAR, or as part of the entire SADAR protocol.

Some of the best times to practice are right after you awake and just as you go to bed. If you spend five minutes breathing deeply and slowly when you go to bed, you will fall asleep quickly and experience a very deep and restful sleep. You awake completely rejuvenated. It has just the opposite effect if you breathe this way when you first get up. It recharges your body, so you are alert and ready to go.

Step 4: Relax your body (Relaxation Therapy)

Tension is a strong indicator of the presence of stress. The longer and more intense you've been exposed to unresolved stress and anxiety, the greater the likelihood tension has resulted in soreness somewhere in your body. This includes headaches and migraines.

Typically, tension is restricted to a specific location or area of the body. You may experience tension in and around your eyes and forehead, jaw, the back of your neck, shoulders, lower back, calves and feet. Scanning your body helps you locate the source(s) of your tension. For those who are very sensitive to stress, tension might be experienced throughout their entire body.

You might already know where you experience tension. If not, moving or massaging those body parts previously mentioned helps you detect affected areas. Go ahead, try it. Massage or move the areas mentioned above to see if you notice any tension or soreness.

Deep relaxation is the opposite of tension. Many Eastern cultures have built lifestyles with relaxation as a foundation for living and peace of mind and body.

All Eastern cultures, although differing in religion and politics, have common grounds in their focus on the art of relaxation. Indian yogis, martial arts masters, Buddhist monks, and even Samurai warriors understand that a mind that can relax the body is a mind that keeps both mind and body strong.

Assignment

Note: *The goal of the routine is to completely relax your entire body with a single thought. Each time you relax a body part, say or think "**relax**". Eventually when you say or think "**relax**" your entire body relaxes automatically.*

- Close your eyes.
- Start with your facial muscles. Be sure your brow is not furrowed. Relax it until the wrinkles in your forehead disappear.
- Place your fingers on the inside of your eyebrows. Gently massage across each eyebrow, starting in the center and moving outwards.
- Next, place your fingers under your eyes and using a circular motion gently massage away any tension.

- Move to the top of your jaw line just under your ears. Gently rub down each side until your fingers meet in the center of your jaw.
- Finish relaxing your facial muscles by massaging both the top and bottom of your ear lobes.
- Any tension in your neck can be released by slowly rotating your neck down, to the right, back, around to the left, and back to center. Then turn your head to the left and hold for a second before turning your head to the right.
- Reduce any tension in your shoulders by making circles with your arms in one direction and then the other.
- Relax your upper and lower back, as well as your chest and abdominal muscles by feeling them release downward. Maintain a straight spine while relaxing these muscles; don't relax them by slouching.
- Observe the muscles in your buttocks and upper legs. They too should feel relaxed, but not numb. Wiggle a little in your seat if either feels tight. You can also alternate tightening and relaxing these muscles until they feel relaxed.
- Your calves, feet, and toes are the last muscles to check Eliminate any tension or numbness in those areas by gently shaking your feet, one at a time. You can also raise your foot off the ground stretching your toes down and then back as far as you can. Do one foot and then the other.

Spend the next five minutes relaxing your body, even if you're not stressed out or anxious. Some people have experienced so much stress and anxiety that they don't realize their body is in a constant state of tension.

Just as with Transformational Breathing, practice this technique by itself until you can relax your body quickly and easily. Because the routine is simple, this should only take three or four repetitions. Practice this routine by itself, in conjunction with Transformational Breathing, or include it as part of the entire SADAR protocol 5-10 times per day, making sure to use it when you go to bed and when you rise.

Remember, the goal is to completely relax your entire body with a single thought. The more you practice, the faster that happens. And don't forget to say **relax** each time you feel relaxed.

Step 5: Smile!!!

If you're like my clients, when you first saw this step you thought, "Smile! What? Are you nuts! How can I smile at a time like this?" You may not want to smile when you're distressed, anxious, frustrated or depressed. Yet, the mere act of turning the ends of your mouth upward releases chemicals known as endorphins into your bloodstream, accelerating your transition from stressed to unstressed or from depressed to happy. Research has documented numerous benefits that smiling produces even if you have no reason to smile. Smiling

- decreases stress and anxiety
- releases endorphins that make you happier
- improves your mood
- strengthens your immune system
- optimizes heart rate
- decreases pain
- reduces aging effects
- improves attention
- increases productivity
- improves success
- makes you more comfortable
- causes people to find you more attractive, approachable, and trustworthy
- produces empathy
- reduces feelings of regret
- is contagious. Not only is your spirit uplifted, so is the spirit of everyone around you.

Assignment

At first, you will want to resist, but once you start smiling, it will be tough to stop. Especially since the next step of SADAR gives you a reason to smile. Smile when you notice someone else smiling.

Smile when you notice others frowning or when you encounter someone who is sad, angry, or frustrated. Use any excuse to smile for no reason.

I guess it's the old "fake it till you make it" approach. Spend the next several minutes smiling for absolutely no reason at all. Then notice how you feel. Has your mood changed? Do you feel lighter or happier? Fantastic! If you need a reason to smile, think about people or events in your life that have brought you joy. Listen to music that makes you smile or watch a funny movie or video, anything that turns that frown upside down. And if that doesn't work, try the next technique.

Step 6: The He-Man Technique

If you have something to smile about, you're more likely to produce a bigger smile; the bigger the smile, the greater the effect. Empowering affirmations, statements of gratitude, or reflections of recent happy moments produce uplifted moods, making it easier to smile. However, the technique I like best is referred to as the He-Man Technique.

Master of Your Inner Universe. The He-Man Technique has worked wonders for many of my clients, especially those who want to transform their emotional state from hopeless or fearful to empowering and energizing. The inclusion of this technique in SADAR resulted from observing my son when he was still quite young as he watched He-Man and the Masters of the Universe.

Regaled in his He-Man costume and carrying a plastic sword, he ran around the house yelling, "I have the power! I have the power!" just like He-Man. I started doing it with him and found that not only did I feel less stress (if I was experiencing any at the time), but my mood soared and felt I could conquer the world. The energy in my body changed completely. No matter how I felt before, my body now was energized.

Try it. Thrust your fist high into the air and shout, "I have the power!". Do it again. "I have the power!" This time shout it three times. "I have the power! I have the power! I have the power!"

I have yet to observe a single client or workshop participant whose emotional state isn't transformed automatically and completely by this theatrical display. Every single person is smiling broadly and having fun.

The reason this one simple phrase works so well is the combined effects of the positive statement and the recruitment of every muscle in your body when you thrust your fist in the air. Now, there are times when you can't thrust your fist in the air and yell "I have the power!". Talk about stress and anxiety from embarrassment.

Mental Rehearsal

If you're in public, you can always close your eyes and imagine thrusting your fist in the air and shouting, "I have the power!" Your subconscious doesn't know the difference between something that's real and the same thing imagined vividly. You experience the same change in mood and energy whether you perform the routine physically or imagine it in your mind.

Try it. Close your eyes and imagine you are He-Man or She-Ra of The Masters of the Universe. Pretend to thrust a defiant fist in the air and hear your imaginary shout, "I have the power!". See yourself do it three times. How do you feel just imagining that you are doing it? Better?

Practice this technique 5-10 times a day. Do not use it when you go to bed as the excitement you feel may make it difficult for you to fall asleep. Use it when you wake up and anytime during the day you feel powerless, stressed out, or anxious. The more you use it, the quicker it improves your mood and energy level.

Step 7: Quiet Eyes

Closing your eyes and taking one or more Transformational Breaths goes a long way to reducing unnecessary visual information and keeping your eyes still. However, there may be times that those two actions may not be enough. The following task not only quiets your eyes, it reconnects the left and right sides of your brain to control your thoughts and emotions. It also reactivates your memory centers and higher cognitive functions.

Assignment: Physical Rehearsal of Sideways-8

- Below find a figure 8 laying on its side, giving the technique its name – Sideways-8
- Place your right index finger in the center of the eight and then **slowly** trace the outline upwards to the right, around the loop and down, back to the center, then upwards to the left, around, down, and back to center.
- Be sure to **watch** your finger trace all the way around the figure, moving upward from the center.
- Repeat this process five times
- Now, repeat the process five times using your left index finger, starting upwards and to the left.

Because you may feel self-conscious performing this technique with others around, you can always perform it in your mind's eye. That is, you can pretend to do it in your mind. Don't worry if you don't see anything. Just pretend that you do.

Mental Rehearsal of Sideways-8

- Close your eyes.
- Imagine a figure 8 that encloses both of your eyes with the bridge of your nose as the center.
- Starting at the bridge of your nose, mentally trace the figure 8 by moving your eyes up and around your right eye, back to center, over and around your left eye, then back down and around to the center.
- Repeat five times.
- Now repeat the process five times, starting up and to the left.

Note: *You may feel your eyes move as you imagine tracing the Sideways-8 around them even when you aren't using your finger to trace around your eyes.*

Spend the next five minutes practicing both physical and the mental rehearsal routines. Then practice either or both 5-10 times per day. You can practice it alone, in conjunction with Transformational Breathing or with the entire SADAR protocol. The more you practice the faster and better it works.

Complete Routine

That's the entire routine. It may seem like a lot, but with very little practice, you will be able to complete the entire routine in your sleep. None of the steps are difficult. It takes no more than five minutes to master each step of the routine. Bundling them together produces the greatest result to effect stress and anxiety. As a reminder, here is the complete routine.

1. Stop
2. Close your eyes (unless you are operating an automobile or dangerous equipment)
3. Transform your breathing
4. Relax your body
5. Smile
6. Change your energy (the He-Man Technique)
7. Quiet your eyes (Sideways-8)

Once you've completed the routine, bring your attention back to the task at hand before opening your eyes. You'll be ready for anything life throws at you. If you're practicing and want to perform the routine more than once, keep your eyes closed and start over.

Assignment

The goal is to become so familiar with the routine that you can do it without thinking about what to do; you just do it. If you practice the routine a minimum of 5-10 times per day for 21-30 consecutive days, you will have no trouble remembering what to do or how to do it. You will become so skilled that it only takes 30-60 seconds to complete.

If you are really committed and continue to use the routine daily, you will reach the point where you use the routine without even knowing you're using it. It's the same way that stress automatically triggers your fight-or-flight reflex when life is not to your liking. After that, you only need to practice it once a day as a reminder to use it when you need it.

You will have rewired your brain to react differently than it does now and will be excited about life because you possess the power to control what you think, how you feel, and what you do regardless of what life throws at you. And if stress and anxiety ever show up – and they will – you have the confidence and skill to know what to do so that it doesn't affect you the way it did in the past. Science refers to this as a conditioning effect.

Classical Conditioning

Are you familiar with Ivan Pavlov? A Russian physiologist, he observed that dogs salivated when fed raw meat. He wondered if he could condition them to salivate in the presence of other stimuli, so he designed an experiment to test his theory. Every time the dogs were fed, they were presented an additional stimulus.

Most people remember Pavlov getting dogs to salivate with the ringing of a bell. Actually, his writings record the use of a wide variety of stimuli, including electric shocks, whistles, metronomes, tuning forks, and a wide range of visual stimuli. Eventually, the dogs salivated in the presence of the sound of a bell or the other stimuli mentioned without being fed. Basically, the dogs' brains were rewired (conditioned) to salivate in the presence of stimuli other than meat.

Over time and with sufficient practice, SADAR rewires your brain, so you engage in positive behaviors in the presence of stressful situations. Of course, just like Pavlov's dogs, it won't happen with just a few attempts. The more you use SADAR, the more powerful its effects and the more automatically it works.

Moving Forward

That's it, just a few short steps that totally transform your experience in stressful situations. Your suffering ends, your mind clears, your nerves calm, and your body is now relaxed and energized. You will be in rest-and-digest and well on your way to achieving a state of peak performance.

There are other techniques and things you can do to improve your chances for success and happiness. Some techniques, like those you just learned, help develop or activate your ability to focus properly on the task at hand. The sideways-8 is used for tasks requiring a narrow-external style of attention. There are three other styles of attention, including wide-external, wide-internal, and narrow-internal. More about these attentional styles, when they're required, and how to develop or activate them can be found in my book, *Stressed to Success: Information, Tools, and Training.*

SADAR stops stress, anxiety, and Negative Programming Cycles as they occur. Every time you intervene using the routine or one of its simple steps, you keep yourself from spiraling down into depression or other forms of mental illness. In Chapter 4, you will learn how to use your imagination to work for you instead of against you. This helps rewire your brain, so things that normally stress you or make you anxious or depressed no longer hold you in their grip.

Summary

• Stress and anxiety affect your vision, ability to think and control your emotions, access to memories, and use of your higher cognitive powers. Fortunately, there are several simple, powerful steps that reverse or even inhibit these destructive effects.

• They include very slow, very deep breathing, relaxing your body, smiling, changing your energy, and quieting your eyes and mind. Together these steps are referred to as the Stress and Anxiety De-Activation Routine or SADAR. They transform your nervous system from fight-or-flight to rest-and-digest. This is the only state where your body can heal itself and you can perform up to your potential.

• SADAR stops any Negative Programming Cycles operating at the time and begins the development of a Positive Programming Cycle.

• For these techniques to work, they must be practiced. Science suggests that doing something 60 times per day for 21 consecutive days is sufficient to retrain your brain.

• If you practice enough, you get to the point where just thinking about the routine changes your reactions in unwanted, aversive situations. Instead of getting stressed and anxious, you become confident and capable. You will be the best you can be.

WOLFMIND

STRONGER IN THE PACK

Chapter 4

Imagination:
The Key to a New You

The true sign of intelligence is not knowledge, but imagination.
- Albert Einstein

In Chapter 3, you were exposed to a very simple yet powerful method, SADAR, that stops stress and anxiety in their tracks. Intervening this way weakens Negative Programming Cycles, so you never begin the downward descent that leads to depression. SADAR is necessary to stop suffering and the fight-or-flight reflex from taking over your life.

To be clear, both the fight-or-flight reflex and Negative Programming Cycles are normal by-products of living in today's complex society. Neither is indicative of poor mental health unless they control your life. Each of us gets stressed, anxious, and engages in negative thinking. Both occur because we've been conditioned to expect life to treat us in very specific ways. We throw tantrums or resign ourselves to a life of restrictions when life doesn't live up to our expectations.

Robert Holden, PhD refers to this as Destination Addiction, *"a preoccupation with the idea that happiness is in the next place, the next job, and with the next partner"*. He goes on to state, *"Until you give up the idea that happiness is somewhere else, it will never be where you are."*

This one belief; the belief that you can't be happy unless everything in your life is 'perfect' or at least the way you want, always causes undue stress. You suffer every time you think about what's missing in your life. The more you want what you don't have, the more you think you'll never get it, the more you suffer.

We hold many other beliefs: social, familial, academic, financial, political, and religious. They result from early programming, our experiences within each of society's institutions, and to some extent, genetic predispositions. But our beliefs are not necessarily true; they are only an interpretation of reality based on these influences. Two people can witness the same event and see something completely different.

If ten people witness an automobile accident, you may get ten different versions of the accident. The funny thing is, not one of them may provide an accurate representation of what happened. Each observer sees the accident through the filters of their beliefs – what they expect would have happened, given their beliefs. Insurance companies seek as many eyewitness reports as possible because they know the reports will differ, reducing their culpability and exposure.

Over time, beliefs become so deep-seated they're taken for absolute truth, including beliefs of who we are. When this happens, thoughts instinctively enter our consciousness about our experiences in the outside world.

Emotional reactions emerge relative to those thoughts. If our beliefs about ourselves, others, and the world are generally negative, so are our thoughts and their resulting emotions.

> *Your beliefs become your thoughts.*
> *Your thoughts become your words.*
> *Your words become your actions.*
> *Your actions become your habits.*
> *Your habits become your values.*
> *Your values become your destiny.*

> *- Mahatma Gandhi*

Altering Dysfunctional Beliefs and Irrational Fears

The way to alter dysfunctional beliefs and eliminate irrational fears is through your imagination. Presently, if you descend into a Negative Programming Cycle or constantly relive your worst nightmares every time life doesn't treat you the way you expect; it's because your imagination goes wild and considers only the worst consequences possible. Now, you will learn how to get your imagination to work for you instead of against you.

You will use the power of your imagination to rewire your brain for happiness and success through very specific routines and the incorporation of concepts that help you view yourself, your situation, and the world differently. These routines have been referred to as **Visualization/Imagery**, **Mental Rehearsal**, **Meditation**, and **Mindfulness**.

Through these practices, you will learn to view yourself and the world differently. Specifically, you will use it to improve your self-esteem, redirect your attention to positive aspects of life, increase your experience of happiness and success, and to lessen the effects memories associated with failure and misery presently exert on your experience of life. Here we refer to these collectively as Mental Rehearsal.

Mental Rehearsal

Mental Rehearsal is the practice of imagining a specific event, utilizing all five senses with the purpose of controlling your internal processes to improve your chances for success in the future. It is such a potent ability that Sport Psychologists consider it the most powerful mental skill athletes can possess. Decades of research confirm their enthusiasm for this ability.

It has also been proven successful in every human activity, including business, academia, the performing arts, and life in general. For example, students who visualize taking a test, seeing themselves relaxed, confident and successful have improved their test-taking abilities. Sales professionals have increased sales quotas after improving their ability to relax and remain focused and confident. Performing artists (actors, dancers, singers, comedians) and business professionals required to give speeches or make presentations or sales pitches have increased their ability to remain calm, focused, and confident in situations where they may have failed in the past.

Of course, it is required that they focus on the **process** that leads to success rather than just seeing a successful outcome. When people focus only on the outcome, the results are mixed at best. Because most of us allow our minds to wander most of the time, it takes considerable practice to develop this skill to its maximum potential.

All practitioners of Mental Rehearsal or Visualization/Imagery first focus on their breathing, observing and reducing physical tension, quieting their minds, and calming their nerves. Sound familiar. It should, it's the same process required in the Stress and Anxiety De-Activation Routine. And you wondered where I got the idea for that routine? I have just systematized it in a way that promotes internal control for optimal success in any situation.

Once in the proper state of mind, simply imagine every important aspect of an event from start to finish, completing the exercise by imagining how great it would feel to be successful or happy. For example, golfers mentally rehearsing successful outcomes while putting would first imagine seeing the size and landscape of the green, including any undulations.

Next, they imagine seeing the golf ball a specific distance from the hole and whether the ball must roll uphill, downhill, or curve left to right or right to left. They imagine their playing partners and any audience in attendance. The smell of grass or flowers that landscape the area as well as what the grass feels like under their feet is imagined. Sounds they normally hear while putting, like the whispers of other golfers or fans watching are also imagined? If they are playing near the ocean, they might taste the salt in the air. Finally, they imagine putting, seeing the ball roll precisely the way they intended, falling into the hole, followed by the exhilaration of success.

Goals of Mental Rehearsal

Few of us ever live in the present.
We are forever anticipating what is to come
or remembering what has gone.

– Louis L'Amour

Approximately 90-95% of our thoughts, emotions, and behaviors are unconscious reactions to what is happening around us and to us. That is, we react without thinking. We don't consciously evaluate the situation before we react to determine if our reactions are in the best interest of the situation. We react based on deep-seated beliefs, attitudes, expectations, and histories in previous similar situations.

This is the definition of living unconsciously or "being asleep at the wheel". It would be okay if our reactions were logical, positive, and uplifting. Unfortunately, because of our genetic predisposition to consider new encounters as potential threats as well as our previous conditioning, we respond emotionally, negatively, and stressfully. These reactions pose a threat to our health, well-being, performance, and experience of life, so much so that the effects have reached epidemic proportions.

Roughly 450 million people worldwide suffer from some form of mental or neurological disorder with more than 350 million of those afflicted with depression; that's 1 in 14 people world-wide that suffer needlessly. Further, it is also estimated that one in four people will suffer from similar mental afflictions sometime in their life. That's staggering! Much of this is attributable to our unconscious reactions to life. Fortunately, it doesn't have to be that way for anyone who decides to take control.

One goal of Mental Rehearsal is to consciously focus on the present without being affected by past regrets or future fears. Other goals include the elimination of stress, anxiety, and Negative Programming Cycles and the development of feelings of hopefulness and personal power that lead to success and happiness. These goals can be accomplished using a variety of different Mental Rehearsal techniques.

Mental Rehearsal as a Form of Mindfulness Training

Because of some of the side effects of antidepressants and antianxiety medication, the predominant approach to treating the consequences of stress, including suicidal thoughts, a worsening of depression, and even death, it's no wonder healthcare professionals are searching for alternative therapies.

Mental Rehearsal teaches people how to respond consciously instead of reacting unconsciously.

In his book, *The Mindful Brain: Reflection and Attunement in the Cultivation of Well-being*, Daniel J. Siegel quotes Jon Kabat-Zinn as defining mindfulness as "The awareness that emerges through paying attention on purpose, in the present moment, and non-judgmentally to the unfolding of experience moment-by-moment." Simply put, mindfulness is being aware of what's happening as its happening. Dr. Siegel is the Director of the Mindful Institute and co-director of the UCLA Mindful Awareness Research Center. Mental Rehearsal is just one form of Mindfulness Training.

Mental Rehearsal as a Form of Meditation

The term meditation refers to a broad variety of practices that includes techniques designed to promote relaxation and build positive internal energy or life force. Other traditions refer to life force as Chi, Ki, or Prana. Meditation is also used to develop certain qualities like compassion, love, patience, generosity, and forgiveness.

The word meditation carries different meanings in different contexts. Meditation has been practiced since antiquity and often involves internal efforts to self-regulate the mind. Meditation is used to clear the mind and ease many health concerns, such as high blood pressure, depression, anxiety and the effects of stress. It can be accomplished both open-eyed and with closed eyes. Meditation doesn't require any specific position or posture to be effective. The same is true of Mental Rehearsal.

In brief, there are dozens of specific styles of meditation practices, and many diverse types of activities commonly referred to as meditative practices. While any of the many forms of meditation can achieve an elevated internal state, we are more interested in Mental Rehearsal for the purposes of comparing one's internal state relative to the present situation and to gain control and assist in promoting a positive outcome, if possible.

Scientifically Proven Benefits

It's now becoming more well-known that Mental Rehearsal, Meditation, and Mindfulness change your brain. The increased calm and quiet you feel is not an imaginary effect. Neuroscientist Dr. Sara Lazar has used brain scans to look at the meditating brain, which shows that long-term meditators have an increased amount of gray matter in the insular and sensory regions. They also have more gray matter in the frontal cortex, an area associated with memory and executive decision-making.

After just eight weeks, people who took part in a mindfulness meditation study, meditating 40 minutes per day, shrunk their amygdala—the part of the brain that governs the fight-or-flight response, and plays a significant role in anxiety, fear, and general stress. A smaller amygdala correlates to reduced stress and anxiety.

Mental Rehearsal, Meditation, and Mindfulness have been scientifically proven to improve the physical health and mental well-being of its practitioners. They tend to be happier, healthier, live longer, and are more accomplished. Their minds are sharper, more attentive, and can be more focused than people who do not engage in these practices. Circulating endorphins, specifically serotonin and dopamine, have been shown to increase through these practices. These practices have been shown to increase gray matter in the brain.

Other studies have reported improvements in the physical health. A new study published in *Cancer* suggests that the mind has a profound influence on the body. Lead investigator, Dr. Linda E. Carlson, and her colleagues found that mindfulness mediation is associated with preserved telomere length in breast cancer patients. Telomeres are protective structures at the end of chromosomes. While their disease-controlling properties are yet to be fully understood, it is known that shortened telomeres are associated with cancer, diabetes, heart disease, high stress levels, and cell-aging whereas longer telomeres are thought to prevent disease.

Other studies have shown that meditators experience reduced pain, stronger immune systems, lower blood pressure, decreased inflammation, and reduced heart risk. A small study conducted in 2003 found a link between an eight-week mindfulness meditation program and better immune function while a 2012 UCLA study suggested meditation improved the immune systems in older people. Studies conducted at Massachusetts General Hospital and the Mayo Clinic suggest that meditation may be helpful in managing high blood pressure, possibly reducing the need for medication.

A 2013 study conducted at the University of Wisconsin-Madison found a possible link between mindfulness meditation and the relief of inflammatory symptoms among people who suffer from chronic inflammation.

As previously mentioned, there are many uses for visualization/ imagery, meditation, and mindfulness training. We will begin our exploration of these practices to improve self-esteem. Poor self-esteem is the greatest effect of a Negative Programming Cycle that starts an individual's descent into depression. Another term used to describe one's acceptance and respect of one's self is self-love. Before we can improve self-esteem, we must first know what it means to love one's self, the consequences of poor self-esteem, and the benefits of learning to love one's self.

The Importance of Self-love

"Love yourself first and everything else falls into line.
You really have to love yourself to get anything done in this world."

- Lucille Ball

Have you ever felt like you weren't good enough? I'll bet you have. We all doubt ourselves from time to time – it's human nature. The crazy thing is we think everyone else is doing better, but it's just not true. Some people fear their inadequacies all the time. In fact, they obsess about it. I know, because that's how I felt for most of my life. Why? I'm not sure.

It could have been a genetic predisposition for low self-esteem, the result of my infant brain unconsciously observing others displaying their own difficulties with self-esteem and unknowingly applying them to myself, or my parents' child-rearing behaviors. It's probably a combination of all of them, but research suggests that interactions with parents and other early caretakers are thought to provide the greatest impact.

Now I was lucky. I came from an intact, two-parent family. My parents loved me and were proud of me and my accomplishments even though they never said so. Some children are not so lucky. Unfortunately for me, my parents grew up believing 'spare the rod, spoil the kid.' They were also raised in an age and culture where boys were not shown physical affection, especially by their fathers. They weren't told they were loved.

Accomplishment was expected as a matter of due course, so no congratulations or rewards for a job well-done were given when they succeeded, but were criticized if they did not meet expectations and punished harshly and disciplined for making mistakes. This is exactly how my parents raised me because it's all they knew. I know my parents had my best interests at heart, doing the best they knew how.

Sadly, I internalized this as rejection; of being unloved, of being unworthy of their love or anyone's love, for that matter. As it started when I was about two, I didn't know how to express the pain and suffering I experienced except through crying. I was spanked and told 'boys don't cry' which only deepened my sadness and feelings of rejection.

To earn my parents' love and respect, I over-achieved. Everything I did was over the top. Because I didn't feel loved by my parents, I didn't feel loved by anyone. I was needy. Achieving success in all aspects of my life was necessary to gain everyone's respect and love. I attempted to please everyone I met in hopes they would like me.

It's probably why I have four degrees, including a bachelor's, two masters, and a doctorate. I also worked hard and excelled at sports. Because love was so important, I searched for and was fortunate to find the 'perfect' love. Only I never felt I deserved it. In my mind, I didn't possess the qualities people respected or found attractive.

I wasn't charismatic or funny, muscular, intelligent or wealthy. I pretended that these didn't matter so others wouldn't recognize my pain.

In the end, I sabotaged every aspect of my life because I was so needy and focused only on myself. My marriage disintegrated, my career faltered, and my health deteriorated. Now don't get me wrong; I don't blame my parents. In fact, I am very grateful to be their son. I know I may not have succeeded to the extent that I have if not for them.

Sadly though, I was plagued with self-doubt and poor self-esteem and suffered fits of depression on-and-off. It was not until I received a PhD in Performance Psychology and earned the American Psychological Association's Dissertation of the Year honors that I finally felt good about myself. Because I felt good about myself, I didn't need or seek approval from others. I went deep inside and realized that I had been my own worst enemy. I was the source of my own pain. Had I accepted and appreciated myself, my interactions with others might have been different.

When that light bulb turned on, my entire world began to change and the most amazing thing occurred. For the first time, I heard my father utter the words, "I'm proud of you son." I was stunned and exhilarated. Because praise was not something he was accustomed to, I could see how uncomfortable he was telling me that. His head was downcast while his eyes stared at the floor. His voice trembled, but I knew he meant it. He did something way out of his comfort zone because it was important to let me know how he felt.

For the first time, I realized that my father truly loved me and wasn't disappointed in me. It gave me a whole new perspective on life. I began to see that other people treated me better than I had treated myself. They probably did my whole life; I just never noticed. And I didn't have to cajole, manipulate, or do anything to earn their friendship and respect. In fact, they had a higher opinion of me than I had of myself.

They say that a boy doesn't become a man until his father dies. I feel very fortunate that I didn't have to wait that long to realize that not only does my father consider me his equal, he looks up to me because I accomplished things he thought he never could. I saw him as a man, not just a god. I still do. He even asks for my opinion and accepts my judgment on things and we have a very different and wonderful relationship.

Helping Others

Using the same tools that I prescribed for others, I cleaned out the perceived skeletons in my closet that haunted me my entire life. As I healed, I became aware of how many people believed as I did; that they were not good enough for the world because they were not good enough for themselves. Like me, they didn't like themselves. Some, so much so, they resist looking at themselves because what they see makes them cringe. They live in self-imposed prisons because no one could live up to the expectations they set for themselves. And I'm talking about successful, socially admired people. Of course, there are many who have not attained much in the way of worldly successes that feel even worse because they keep comparing themselves to those who have achieved more.

What is Self-love?

Before defining self-love let me tell you what it is not. In the Judeo-Christian culture, we are taught that self-love is narcissistic, and therefore, a sin. Narcissism is synonymous with selfishness, egotism, and self-absorption. I don't think this is what Jesus had in mind when He taught that one of the two greatest commandments is to "love your neighbor as yourself". Of course, the other commandment is to "love God above all else".

I don't think a narcissist loves God above all else and I don't think Jesus would tell us to love others as we love ourselves if He didn't think it important that we love ourselves. How can we love others if we don't love ourselves? Based on His words, if we don't love ourselves then we shouldn't love others. I don't think that's what He had in mind. I believe that He was speaking about Divine love; a love that shows respect for ourselves and others, a love that doesn't judge anyone for supposed failings, a love that considers everyone equal and connected.

Divine love is an acceptance of who you are; it is a basic respect for your very existence. When you love yourself Divinely, your strengths far outweigh any weaknesses you think you have. You are not obsessed with trying to please others just so they will like you or try to manipulate or control others to advance your own agenda. It doesn't look for sympathy, nor is it concerned with feeling superior.

Because you are not obsessed with yourself, you focus on helping others. You're concerned about their needs, but not to the point that it's detrimental to your health or well-being. You don't rationalize your behaviors or engage in blame, shame, and guilt, rather you take responsibility for your actions and let others take responsibility for theirs. You love yourself and others the way God loves us all; Divinely, forgiving others their trespasses and being grateful to have them in your life.

If you disagree with anyone about anything, you work it out, just as Jesus taught us to do. You don't consider others' judgments of you above your own. If a behavior no longer serves you, you change it to make your life better, not to please others. Your beliefs, thoughts, emotions, and behaviors are to everyone's benefit.

You are perfect just as you are; not in spite of your flaws, but because of them. They make you the perfect expression of love your Creator intended.

- Dr. Anthony Piparo

Habits of Individuals with Poor Self-esteem.

Self-esteem or self-worth are terms normally used to describe your sense of self or ability to love yourself. People with low self-esteem or self-worth tend to be miserable. Here are just some of the habits of miserable people.

- They have a negative self-concept.
- They experience fear in most parts of their lives.
- They pick fights with others just to prove they're right, speaking loudly over the top of everyone to drown them out or bully them to feel righteous.

- They blame, shame, and guilt others and themselves for perceived failings.
- They do everything for personal gain.
- They look for sympathy.
- They are self-absorbed with what others think of them.
- They are not grateful for blessings, large or small.
- They're in constant state of alertness because something can go wrong.
- They tend to be anxious.
- They justify their behaviors when they make mistakes.
- They worry about their problems and look for obstacles instead of solutions.
- They either glorify or vilify the past. It's all or nothing.
- They expect the future to be as bad as or worse than the present and the present isn't a picnic.
- They try to reform others.
- They consider the needs of others to be more important than their own to the point of the detriment of their emotional and physical health.
- They are either always right or always wrong.
- They constantly seek approval.

Compare this to people with a healthy sense of self; to people who like and respect themselves

Habits of Self-loving People

- They possess a positive self-identity.
- They have time to help others because they are not focused on projecting a positive image to get others to like them.
- They don't self-sabotage.
- They feel deserving of good fortune.
- They appreciate and grateful for what they have and the people in their lives.
- They see the big picture and don't focus on minutia that interferes with their progress.
- They invest in their dreams.
- They have more fun and enjoy life.
- They live in the present

- They associate with other happy people.
- They do for others without expecting anything in return.
- They forgive themselves and others for their failings.
- They focus on their strengths.
- They take responsibility for their actions and allow others to take responsibility for theirs.
- They say, "I'm sorry" when they make mistakes or hurt others.
- They don't feel superior.
- They accept others just as they are.
- They're comfortable with themselves and don't feel lonely when alone.
- They set healthy boundaries and can say no when necessary.

Scientific benefits associated with people who possess healthy self-concepts

Scientists have conducted considerable research comparing people possessing positive self-esteems with people who possess poor self-concepts. They conclude that people who value themselves tend to be happier, healthier both mentally and physically, are more successful, and have better relationships. They also tend to eat and sleep better. They have more time for themselves and others. They treat themselves and others with more compassion. They get things done and don't procrastinate. They do better in times of adversity and find healthy ways to get through tough situations.

Assignment

Please review the two lists above and check each behavior that applies to your life. The more items you check from the first list, the more you dislike yourself, and the more you must do to improve your self-image.

Every time you doubt yourself or think that you're deficient in any way - STOP. Complete at least one repetition of SADAR, then smile for at least thirty seconds. While you smile, repeat one or more of the affirmations found below. Or you may want to create your own. If you experience a lot of difficulty with self-worth, keep a note card with these affirmations with you.

Spend 30 minutes a day learning to love yourself. You don't have to perform this routine for 30 minutes all at once. You can break up your practice into 2-3 shorter sessions if you want. You still gain the same benefit if you do.

Self-loving Affirmations (Mantras)

- I love being me.
- I am worthy of all the blessings I receive.
- I accept, love, revere, and celebrate all that I am.
- I am love and loved.
- My love streams outward from my heart, encompassing every heart in the universe.
- I choose love and love chooses me.
- My love is Divine.
- Because I am a child of the Divine, I am Divine and so are you.
- I'm perfect just as I am because God doesn't create anything that isn't perfect.
- My love is infinite.
- I look inside for wisdom.
- I am completely worthy in this moment and every moment.
- I give love and I receive love.

Gratitude

Gratitude is not only a virtue, but it also is part of a practical philosophy of daily life. There is no wiser way of living than to remember every morning what Life has given us, and to lift up our thoughts in thankfulness for every bounty we possess.

Ernest Holmes, The Science of Mind

It's no secret that stress makes us sick, particularly when we can't cope with it. It's linked to several leading causes of death, including heart disease and cancer, and claims responsibility for up to 90% of all doctor visits. Gratitude, it turns out, helps us better manage stress. Gratitude has long been extolled by religion and, in recent years, has drawn attention to books such as *The Simple Abundance Journal of Gratitude,* by Sarah Ban Breathnach. Recent research on gratitude suggests that feelings of thankfulness produce tremendous positive value in helping people cope with daily problems, especially stress.

The word gratitude is derived from the Latin word gratia, which means grace, graciousness, or gratefulness. In some ways, gratitude encompasses all three meanings. Gratitude is a thankful appreciation for what an individual receives, whether tangible or intangible. With gratitude, people acknowledge the goodness in their lives. In the process, they recognize the source of that goodness lies at least partially outside themselves. As a result, gratitude helps people reconnect with something larger than themselves, whether to other people, nature, or a higher power.

People feel and express gratitude in multiple ways. They may apply it to the past (retrieving positive memories and being grateful for past blessings), the present (not taking good fortune for granted), and the future (maintaining a hopeful and optimistic attitude). Regardless of the inherent or current level of gratitude, it's a quality you can successfully cultivate further.

Benefits

Dr. P. Murali Doraiswamy, head of the division of biologic psychology at Duke University Medical Center once stated, *"If [thankfulness] were a drug, it would be the world's best-selling product with a health maintenance indication for every major organ system."* As noted in an ABC News article, studies have shown that gratitude produces numerous measurable effects, including improvements in mood-enhancing neurotransmitters like serotonin and dopamine, reductions in inflammation, improved immune systems, increases in testosterone, reductions in stress hormones, increases in oxytocin (a social bonding hormone), decreases in blood pressure and improvements in cardiac and EEG rhythms, as well as optimal blood sugar levels.

Much of the research on gratitude is summarized in the book by Robert A. Emmons, PhD, *Thanks!: How the New Science of Gratitude Can Make You Happier*. Emmons and his colleagues at the University of California, Davis are part of a larger movement called positive psychology. Instead of focusing on illness and emotional problems, positive psychology studies health-promoting behaviors and the pleasurable aspects of life.

Summarizing findings from the research to date, Emmons reports that those practicing gratitude reap emotional, physical, and interpersonal benefits. People who regularly keep a gratitude journal report fewer symptoms, feel better about their lives, and are more optimistic about the future. Emmons concludes that gratitude is a choice; one possible response to life experiences. The choice to experience gratitude for even the most painful of experiences can be developed through continued daily practice.

Let gratitude be the pillow upon which you kneel
to say your nightly prayer.

Maya Angelou

Grateful people, those who perceive gratitude as a permanent trait rather than a temporary state of mind, have an edge on the not-so-grateful when it comes to health. Grateful people take better care of themselves and engage in more protective health behaviors like regular exercise, a healthy diet, and regular physical examinations. Other benefits of cultivating the daily life habit of gratitude include increases in psychological well-being, mental strength, self-confidence and self-esteem, enhanced empathy, and reduced aggression. It also opens the door to better relationships, improved physical health and sleep, all of which result in greater energy during the day.

God gave you a gift of 86,400 seconds today.
Have you used one to say thank you?

William Arthur Ward

Assignment 1

Below, please list people and experiences you are grateful for, but never think about. My list includes beautiful sunrises and sunsets, warm sunny days, my children, other family members, friends, and my health.

_____

_____

_____

_____

Assignment 2

Feeling grateful for those who treat us poorly; whose values differ from ours, or for undesirable, challenging, or aversive situations is not easy. It's something that must continually be worked on. For the next thirty days, focus on cultivating the quality of gratitude for any person or situation for which you now feel anything but grateful. Below, list five positive qualities for anyone you do not see eye-to-eye with. They might be loving parents, hard workers, or committed to whatever political or religious beliefs they hold even if they differ from your own.

_____

_____

_____

_____

Each day choose one person. The person you choose can be the same day-after-day or someone new each day. Repeat at least one repetition of SADAR, then continue smiling for the next 30-60 seconds, focused on the positive qualities possessed by the person or group you're in conflict with. Afterward, think or say the following.

"I am so happy and grateful for_____. He or she is _____." (List each of the positive qualities you listed above.)

Finish by taking another slow, deep breath, and smiling until your aggravation subsides. It may take you longer than thirty days, so continue using the exercise until you no longer are emotionally affected by the person, group, institution, or situation. Because life is not always fun, people and situations will continue to try and pull you back into their drama. Remain vigilant. At the first sign of negative feelings or thoughts – STOP. Use the above exercise to recompose yourself.

Hardwiring Your Subconscious for Happiness

Thousands of years of surviving hostile environments has endowed humans with a Negativity Bias that protects us in times of physical threat. The more a child is surrounded by adults who react to stressful situations emotionally and have suffered through misery and other social stresses, the more their natural Negativity Bias is reinforced. But science has proven that a Negativity Bias, no matter how strong, can be replaced, or at least diminished in strength through Meditation, Mindfulness Training or Visualization/Imagery.

Once you have significantly internalized SADAR you can begin the process of hardwiring your subconscious for happiness. This may take up to a week or more. Have fun with it. Your fantasies should instill a sense of peace, fun, creativity, and enjoyment.

Assignment

Write out your ideal vacation. Mine would be a trip to the beach. Be sure to write out everything you would experience with all five senses. After having selected your fantasy trip, perform one repetition of SADAR. Introduce such emotions as joy, serenity, happiness, freedom, or excitement and then go on "vacation".

Your fantasy may last up to 30 minutes or more. I always "meditated" just as I got into bed. Most times I fell asleep long before my vacation ended. That's okay if it happens to you, too. Sleep is a positive sign that you have become quite peaceful.

Hardwiring Your Brain for Success

Remember, if you are obsessed with past mistakes and failures, you eventually descend into a state of depression, if you haven't already done so. You can't see yourself succeeding in the future, no matter how hard you try. That's because you are in a state of fight-or-flight spiraling down through a destructive Negative Programming Cycle.

To be able to begin to see yourself as successful, your mind must be clear, your nerves calmed, and your body relaxed and energized.

Assignment

Spend 30 minutes reviewing your upcoming schedule, choosing events where it's important for you to succeed. Choose one event and write out exactly where this event takes place, including everything you might see, feel, hear, smell, and taste in that environment. What do you hope to accomplish? In other words, what do you define as "successful" in this situation?

1. Using SADAR, clear your mind, calm your nerves, and relax and energize your body.

2. Start imagining the event from start to finish.

3. If you have difficulty visualizing this event the way you want – STOP – repeat SADAR and then return to your success fantasy.

4. When you can complete the assignment exactly the way you desire, shout (out loud or to yourself) "I did it! I succeeded! How great am I?".

5. Perform this routine every day for the next 30 days and then at least 1-2 times per week every week thereafter.

Overcoming Memories of Failure and Misery

The Recall/Rewrite Protocol

Normally, I don't allow people to relive old wounds. This is the one exception. I don't recommend the Recall/Rewrite protocol until the client has extensive experience in using SADAR and can quickly alter their internal reality. I don't believe it is in anyone's best interest to suffer needlessly.

You need to return quickly to a state of rest-and-digest once the painful memory of a recent failure or misery has put you in fight-or-flight.

Assignment

1. Write out the details of a previous failure or stressful incident. Try to remember what you saw, heard, felt, smelled, and tasted as well as your thoughts and emotions around the event. As you write, notice how you feel and if you become distracted.

2. Use SADAR to quiet your mind and calm your nerves.

3. Now write a new script where you are successful, happy, exhilarated or inspired in a "made for TV" version of the same event. Again, you play the lead in this updated version. After writing the new script, notice what you're thinking and feeling. Is it what you want?

4. Rehearse this daily. The goal is to reach the point that when you remember previous failures, you don't experience emotional trauma. Instead, you smile and think, "That's not me. I'm successful. I'm confident! Bring it on!"

For the next 30 days, recall the original script allowing yourself to become distressed as if you were reliving the event. This shouldn't take more than 30-60 seconds. Quickly employ SADAR, completing as many repetitions as is necessary to calm your mind and nerves completely. Now pull out the new script; the rewrite of the old script where you are successful, happy, exhilarated, inspired, or motivated.

Because the experience may be new to you, you may not completely embrace or believe life could be this way. That's okay. Don't stop. Continue using the protocol until you alter your internal reality quickly and easily and until you believe that this experience is not only possible, but within your power and control to produce on demand.

You will notice that you're happier and feel more successful, even when you fail. You'll be smiling almost non-stop. Now isn't life supposed to be that way? My attitude is, "This is the only life I get, why would I **not** want to live it in a state of happiness, believing I'm successful and respected, no matter what the world tries to sell me?"

Moving forward

In the first four chapters of this book, you learned what depression is, how it develops, as well as some of the dire consequences of not treating it correctly. You also learned about a run-away fight-or-flight reflex and Negative Programming Cycles, the two true predictors of those of who eventually succumb to the ravages of depression. More importantly, you were exposed to two alternative methods for treating depression, SADAR and your imagination.

SADAR purges your body of fight-or-flight hormones that, if left unabated, eventually compromise your life, health, and productivity. By intervening in the fight-or-flight process, you stop any Negative Programming Cycle operating at the time. The more you intervene, the less likely you will descend into the depression that defines so many peoples' lives.

Your imagination can work for or against you. Using the tools in this chapter, you begin to wire your brain in ways that improve how your imagination affects your life. But your process of healing is not complete. There are other considerations that must be explored that determine the extent to which you become mentally and emotionally healthy.

These considerations include sleep, nutrition, and exercise. Improving these areas of your life increases the speed of your recovery. Finally, you must design an Action Plan to affect all areas of your life involved in how you experience life.

Summary

- Happiness and success are states of being. They are choices you make daily about who you are and what you want to experience, regardless of what the world tries to tell you.

- Imagination is your key to creating the success and happiness that has eluded you in the past.

- For most people, their imagination hijacks their desires for success and happiness because they have been conditioned to believe that these things aren't possible and their experiences in life mirror those conditioned beliefs.

- Visualization/Imagery, Meditation, and Mindfulness Training are three methods for tapping into your powers of imagination to get it to work for you instead of against you.

- These methods take advantage of the human superpower, neuroplasticity.

- If you continue reacting to life the way you have in the past, you strengthen the existing telecommunication system that is responsible for your pain, suffering, and depression.

- If you decide to change, the methods described in this chapter help rewire your brain for success and happiness.

- You can never change what you experience in the outside world until you change what you experience internally.

WOLFMIND

STRONGER IN THE PACK

Chapter 5
Upgrading Your Life

After being diagnosed with depression and several other co-occurring conditions, I knew something needed to be done. Having resisted the recommendations of my physicians to use prescriptive medications to treat my illnesses and not finding cognitive therapy to help, I sought alternative approaches for my deteriorating physical and mental health. Fortunately, by the grace of God, I met the right people who led me out of the cavern of depression I now called home.

I had been exposed to the concepts and actions that improved my mental and physical health. The only thing left to tackle were lifestyle choices that contributed to my poor health. In this chapter, you will learn about the effects that sleep, diet, and level of physical activity exert on your experiences of life. You will determine how they affect you and if your life needs to be upgraded. There are other factors that contribute to stress, anxiety, and depression. You can learn more about these in my book, *Stressed to Success: Upgrading Your Life.*

Sleep

Sleep is incredibly important. Sleep deprivation is both a cause and byproduct of prolonged exposure to unresolved stress and may lead to depression. In the short term, sufferers experience decreased performance and alertness, memory loss and cognitive impairment, an inability to participate in certain daily activities that require sustained attention, increased risk for injury, and automotive accidents.

Long-term sleep disorders lead to high blood pressure, heart attack, heart failure, stroke, obesity, psychiatric problems, including **depression** and other mood disorders, Attention Deficit Disorder (ADD), mental impairment, as well as fetal and childhood growth retardation.

Do you experience sleep problems? Do you find yourself fatigued throughout the day? Is your lack of sleep caused by stress and anxiety? Is it caused by your choice to stay up late and get up early? The reasons you don't get enough sleep determines your course of action.

There are several options available to you if sleep deprivation is the result of stress and anxiety. We will explore these options, so you fall asleep quickly and stay asleep and get the rest you need to be successful and vibrant. If your lack of sleep is the result of lifestyle choices, you will have to decide if it's in your best interest to change your sleep patterns.

Let's see if you're presently getting enough sleep. The National Sleep Foundation has outlined the amount of sleep each of us should get daily, depending on our age. Below, find their published sleep standards:

• Older adults (65 years old and above)	7-8 hours
• Adults (24-65 years old)	7-9 hours
• Young Adults (18-25 years old)	7-9 hours
• Teenagers (14-17 years old)	8-10 hours
• School-age children (6-13 years old)	9-11 hours
• Preschool children (3-5 years old)	10-13 hours
• Toddlers (1-2 years old)	11-14 hours
• Infants (4-11 months)	12-15 hours
• Newborns (0-3 months)	14-17 hours

Causes of Sleep Deprivation

Are you getting enough sleep? If not, let's examine some of the primary reasons people don't get sufficient **restful** sleep. You already know that stress and anxiety are primary culprits. Let's see if any of your daily habits contribute to your sleep deprivation.

Technology

Electronic devices, including laptops, cell phones, and TVs, all give off light that mess with your body's production of melatonin. Melatonin is the hormone that helps you fall asleep. Electronic devices interfere with sleep because your mind is tuned into it even when it's off. That is, you're programmed to listen for incoming messages. Your subconscious is on alert, waking you at regular or not so regular intervals to check.

Simple Solutions. Here are some things to do to keep your smart phone from interfering with your sleep. Keep it in the kitchen, den, or bathroom to recharge. Don't keep it on your nightstand or anywhere in your bedroom where you'll be tempted to check it after lights out.

To break the subconscious habit of waiting for messages, be sure to use SADAR when you go to bed. Hopefully, you're already doing this. SADAR helps break obsessive patterns by redirecting thoughts and relaxing your mind and body.

Bedtime Snacks

Most of us have developed the habit of eating just prior to going to bed. If this is you and it affects your ability to fall asleep or stay asleep, you want to determine if that is something that needs upgrading. Below find foods that disrupt sleep as well as foods that promote restful sleep.

Sleep Disrupting Foods

- Foods high in refined carbohydrates like chips, pretzels, and tacos
- Foods high in protein like red meat
- Fried foods
- Foods high in saturated fats like bacon
- Carbonated drinks (regular or diet)
- Spicy foods
- Sugary foods
- Caffeine
- Alcohol
- Even healthy foods like grapefruit, celery, cucumbers, tomatoes, beans, watermelon, radishes, and broccoli can keep you up when you want to sleep.

Sleep Inducing Foods

- Popcorn (plain with very little salt and no added butter, margarine, or oil of any kind)
- Kale chips
- Turkey
- Mango
- Dark or tart cherries (fresh, dried, or juiced, my favorite)
- Dried garbanzo (chick) peas
- Bananas
- Milk
- Yogurt
- Almond or peanut butter
- Whole wheat crackers
- Chamomile tea
- Honey

Simple Solutions. Keep this list where you can find it. If you're presently eating something that's not on the list, do an Internet search to determine its effect on sleep. Add it to whichever list it applies. The advice is very simple; eat foods associated with deep sleep and avoid foods that disrupt sleep within the last couple of hours before bedtime.

Environmental Sleep Disrupters

Sleep may also be disrupted by things in your room. Too much noise or light exert a strong influence on sleep patterns. Be sure that your room is dark and away from any noise. Things like TV and loud music can keep you awake, so too can room temperature. Turn off the television and music at least 1-2 hours prior to going to bed. Sleep researchers find that 65-75 degrees Fahrenheit is the best range for sleep.

The Stress of a Sedentary Life

A body in motion stays in motion; a body at rest will remain at rest
Sir Isaac Newton

Newton's first law of physics is not only applicable to objects traveling through space, it's true for human activity as well. People who are physically active find it easy to get themselves off the couch and get moving. In fact, they rarely find themselves sitting for any length of time. Individuals who lead sedentary lives find it an almost impossible challenge to become physically active or exercise. Unfortunately, overwhelming agreement among researchers into the connection between physical activity and health is not good news for those of us who like to call the couch home.

In addition, research has found that lack of exercise and physical activity is twice as likely to shorten your life as obesity. Even people who exercise regularly may be at significant risk to die prematurely if they sit for more than eight hours per day. Dr. Joseph Mercola, an alternative medicine proponent and osteopath, recommends sitting for no more than three hours per day. He also recommends walking 7,000-10,000 steps per day in addition to a normal workout routine.

The connection between low-energy level activities that involve prolonged sitting and an increased risk for anxiety has been well-documented. Dr. Megan Teychenne, head researcher and lecturer in Physical Activity and Health in the School of Exercise and Nutrition Sciences at Deakin University in Australia and her colleagues analyzed the results of nine separate studies. They discovered that in five of these studies, there was a positive relationship between prolonged sitting and an increased risk of anxiety while four studies showed that longer total sitting times were associated with higher levels of anxiety.

In 1992, I designed a study to examine *"The Chronic Effects of Fitness on Concentration and Performance"*. While subjects performed a golf putting task, the results provided far-reaching applications. Subjects were stressed by having to perform one or two additional tasks immediately prior to putting.

Both tasks were related to memory. Prior to putting in one of the trials, participants were read a seven-digit number. As soon as they putted they had to verbally repeat that number. The other task required memory, but also required a physical response immediately prior to putting. Subjects listened for a random set of differently pitched sounds (low or high) as they prepared to putt, then had to depress the appropriate buttons, located just below their hands.

Results showed that the subjects who exercised on a regular basis outperformed non-exercisers. The more stress involved in the task, the better exercisers performed. Non-exercisers did their best when they either putted or completed one of the memory tasks. Exercisers outperformed non-exercisers on both physical and attentional tasks and the difference in performance increased as the stress of the task increased.

This was the first study to examine the chronic effects of fitness on concentration and performance. It demonstrated the superiority of exercisers when it comes to handling stress in sedentary activities. Putting doesn't require strength, speed, or stamina; neither did the two memory tasks. All participants reported being highly stressed when the memory tasks were added to the putting task.

My study didn't uncover the mechanism by which exercise facilitates concentration and performance under duress. We theorized that one of two mechanisms was responsible for the difference between exercisers and non-exercisers. One explanation was that exercise immunizes participants from stress. In other words, there may be a change in physiology that provides exercisers with the ability to ward off the effects of stress.

The other explanation was that a training effect occurred. Exercisers learn to handle stress by constantly stressing their bodies through exercise, helping them handle psycho-social stress as well. Research since that time has found that stress is mediated both through physiological changes and training effects.

Benefits of Exercise and Physical Activity

If you must sit a lot during the day, it's best to stand up periodically. The simple act of standing yields many benefits. Molecular and cellular systems responsible for regulating blood sugar levels, triglyceride, and cholesterol, all of which are mediated by insulin, become active within 90 seconds of standing. These changes occur simply by shifting your body weight from your back side to your legs. The simple act of standing pushes fuels into your cells, radically decreasing your risk of diabetes and obesity.

According to Dr. James A. Levine, co-director of the Mayo Clinic/ Arizona State University Obesity Solutions Initiative, and author of *Get Up!: Why Your Chair is Killing You and What You Can Do About It*, the human body was designed to be active all-day long. Sitting is not supposed to be a way of life. Stop moving for extended periods and your body starts shutting down.

Sitting switches off basic cellular fueling systems that integrate what's going on in your bloodstream with what's going on in your muscles, increasing blood sugar levels, cholesterol, and blood pressure. Basically, prolonged inactivity causes your internal systems to think that death is imminent and starts preparing for that eventuality.

In addition to reducing the risk for obesity and type 2 diabetes, exercise reduces the risk for heart disease and improves brain health into old age. Mounting research shows that exercise is as important for brain function as it is for the rest of the body. Increased blood flow improves brain function almost immediately and prompts growth of new brain cells in the hippocampus; that part of the brain used to boost memory, learning, and mood regulation.

Exercise produces changes in your DNA that protect against such diseases as dementia, Alzheimer's and Parkinson's by triggering the release of endorphins, serotonin, dopamine, glutamate, and GABA (γ-Aminobutyric acid). GABA is the chief inhibitory neurotransmitter in the mammalian central nervous system, playing a significant role in reducing neuronal excitability throughout the nervous system. In humans, GABA is also directly responsible for the regulation of muscle tone. These neurotransmitters are well-known for their role in regulating mood. Not surprisingly, exercise is effective in the prevention and treatment of **depression** and stress relief.

In general, exercise improves connectivity of brain circuitry, increases gray matter, combats and reverses brain shrinkage associated with aging, increases performance on cognitive tasks, and shields you from stress and depression.

Moving your body increases blood flow to your brain which elevates oxygen levels, triggering biochemical changes that protect the new resulting neurons (gray matter) by bathing them in BDNF.

BDNF or brain-derived neurotrophic factor is a protein and a member of a family of growth factors related to the canonical nerve growth factor. These conditions encourage your brain to grow and change by forming new neural pathways and synaptic connections. You know this as neuroplasticity. People who stay physically active into old age show improved cognitive function by preventing the decline of the brain's white matter, fiber-like parts of brain cells that enable communication between brain regions.

The Intensity of Physical Activity Necessary to Produce Benefits

You don't have to sweat and grunt for hours-on-end to experience the benefits of physical activity and exercise. Moderate physical activity produces the greatest health and well-being benefits. If you have not been physically active for awhile and are basically out-of-shape, it is highly recommended you start slow and easy, increasing the time and intensity of your workout as your body habituates to the increased physical output.

What Types of Activities Produce the Greatest Benefits

Activities like yoga, t'ai chi ch'uan, and Qigong require learning complex movement patterns. They also require learning to coordinate complex movement patterns with slow, deliberate breathing patterns. Intellectual or physical activities that require learning complex information stimulates the brain helping it develop new structures to remember the information. Complex physical training activates the human superpower, neuroplasticity.

One study conducted by German researchers found that high school students who performed 10 minutes of a complex movement pattern outperformed students who performed 10 minutes of a less complex exercise on an attentional task requiring higher levels of concentration. Students who didn't exercise at all performed the worst on the attentional task.

According to new research, activities like yoga may be instrumental in preventing and reversing anatomical changes and impairments that chronic pain causes in the brain. According to M. Catherine Bushnell, PhD, the Scientific Director of the Division of Intramural Research for the National Institutes of Health (NIH), many chronic pain patients suffer from anxiety and depression as well as deficits in cognitive functioning. She goes on to show that brains of patients who suffer from multiple sources of chronic pain differ from healthy control subjects.

Research has found that people with depression have reduced gray matter. Decreased gray matter leads to memory impairment, emotional problems, and decreased cognitive functioning. Bushnell also stated that there is compelling evidence from studies conducted at NIH and other institutions that mind-body techniques, such as yoga and meditation, counteract the brain anatomy effects of chronic pain. While speaking at the American Pain Society's annual meeting, Bushnell stated that long-time teachers of yoga are found to have more gray matter in multiple brain regions. Practicing yoga regularly produces the opposite effect on the brain than does chronic pain.

Yoga practitioners have more gray matter in multiple brain regions. Some gray matter increases correspond to the duration of yoga practice, which suggests there is a causative link between yoga and the increase of gray matter. Brain anatomy changes may contribute to mood disorders and other affective cognitive problems associated with chronic pain. Mind-body practices like yoga seem to exert a protective effect on brain gray matter that counteract the neuroanatomical effects of chronic pain.

The Time Necessary to Produce Benefits

You don't have to spend hours in the gym to reap the health and stress-relief benefits of exercise and physical activity. Thirty minutes, 3-4 times per week of moderate activity (just enough effort to get you breathing a little faster) produces huge benefits. However, remember the advice of Dr. James Levine and Dr. Joseph Mercola. The human body was not designed for inactivity. On the contrary, we were designed to be active. Just imagine what our hunter and gatherer ancestors had to go through.

It wasn't until we became an agrarian society, where there was more opportunity for inactivity, that humans started gaining weight and getting sick with illnesses that didn't exist until that time. In addition to the amount of time engaged in physical activity that gets us breathing a little faster, we must get off our butts every hour, so our body doesn't think it's dying and throw our internal systems out-of-whack.

Before embarking on an exercise regime, please contact your physician to determine if you are fit enough to exercise and for advice about duration, intensity, and type of exercise that may be most suited to your present condition.

Assignment

1. If you must sit at a desk for prolonged periods of time, get up hourly; stretch, walk in place, or around the office, or just move about for 90 seconds or more. Remember the benefits you receive when you carry your weight on your legs instead of your butt.

2. Park as far away from your office as possible, so you get some exercise coming to and leaving the office.

3. Take the stairs instead of the elevator, unless you must walk up more than a few flights.

4. If you spend too much time in front of the television, get up during the commercials, stretch, or walk in place or from room to room until your program comes back on. You can also stand when the commercial comes on and sit when it turns off.

5. If you spend copious amounts of time in front of a computer it is best if you stand up and engage in some form of physical activity or exercise hourly. Stretch, walk around, or perform a few yoga exercises or Qigong movements.

6. Go for a walk instead of watching television. Much of your fatigue results from stress as well as from sitting too long. Walking, whether it's a stroll, fast, or a combination of fast

and slow improves your stamina. This increase in stamina improves your ability to overcome stress. Once you develop the habit of moving, feel-good hormones released into your bloodstream make you want to be more active. You won't feel good sitting and you will become antsy just to shake your booty.

Dietary Distress

You are what you eat.

Jean Anthelme Brillat-Savarin

Are you a McDonald's cheeseburger or Big Mac, another fast food meal, or are you something healthy? You are what you eat and what you eat is important for health and overall brain function. The healthier you eat, the better your brain function, performance, health, and life in general.

Jean Anthelme Brillat-Savarin (1755–1826), a French lawyer, politician, epicure, and gastronome originally wrote, "Dis-moi ce que tu manges, je te dirai ce que tu es" which translates into English as "Tell me what you eat, and I will tell you what you are." The next known reference appeared in an essay entitled *On Spiritualism and Materialism* in 1863/64, written by Ludwig Andreas Feuerbach, a German philosopher and anthropologist. He wrote, "Der Mensch ist, was er ißt." or "Man is what he eats."

The first known English reference appeared sometime in the 1920's or '30's on a radio show hosted by nutritionist Dr. Victor Lindlahr who promoted a catabolic diet. Eventually, he published his thesis on the connection between food and health in his book, *You are What You Eat: How to Win and Keep Health with Diet*. Lindlahr's mantra was once again brought to life during the hippie era of the 1960's to promote the benefits of a macrobiotic wholefood diet.

The connection between food and health has been known for eons. Five thousand years ago, Chinese Taoists recommended a diet that consisted of 50-75% fruits and vegetables. Somehow, the connection was lost and doesn't seem to be taught at any length in medical schools even though Hippocrates, considered the father of Western medicine (physicians are required to take the Hippocratic Oath) wrote, "Let food be thy medicine and medicine be thy food." Recent research confirms the relationship between diet and health.

Because food manufacturers hide these facts and lie about the supposed health benefits of their foods, most people do not know what foods to eat. Processed food manufacturers load their products with salt, sugar, MSG, and other chemicals that are just as addictive as illicit drugs. We go through withdrawal every time these foods leave our system the way drug addicts go through withdrawal when drugs leave their system, leaving us craving more.

Healthy Foods

- Whole grains
- Oily fish
- Organic fresh fruits
- Organic fresh vegetables
- Raw nuts
- Legumes
- Leafy greens
- Sunflower seeds
- Coconut oil
- Olive oil
- Oatmeal
- Grass fed beef
- Range free organic chicken and eggs

Unhealthy Foods

- Processed foods
- Fast food
- Junk food
- Sugary foods
- Artificially-sweetened foods
- Fried foods
- Foods containing trans-fats
- Cold cereals
- Wheat and gluten
- Most dairy

- Conventionally raised meats
- Conventionally grown produce
- Foods with ingredients you can't pronounce

Brain Health. Good nutrition is key to maintaining a healthy brain throughout your life. Fueling your brain with fat encourages ketosis, providing energy to the brain and protecting you against brain disease. A diet high in monounsaturated fats increases production of acetylcholine, a neurotransmitter important for learning and memory.

Polyunsaturated fats contain the essential fatty acids (EFAs) omega-3 and omega-6 that our brains need to function properly and are linked to reduced rates of **major depression**. Unfortunately, humans are unable to produce EFAs, so they must be included in our diet. DHA, another omega-3 fatty acid, has been shown to assist brain function. Increasing dietary levels of omega-3 has been shown to help improve such conditions as **depression, bipolar disorder**, and **ADHD**.

Saturated fat is one of the main components of brain cells and is therefore necessary for healthy brain function. One study found that people who ate more saturated fat reduced their risk of developing dementia by 36%. Saturated fat also benefits the liver and immune system and helps maintain proper hormone balance. So would you rather be an apple or a candy apple? Remember you are what you eat. Eating healthy food exerts powerful influences on your ability to prevent or recover from depression.

Overcoming Food Addictions

Many people don't think of themselves as addicted to food. All the time I hear, "I like the taste of _____." (Add whatever unhealthy food you think tastes so good you couldn't live without.) "I couldn't get through the day without coffee." Anytime you must have something and you can't even consider the possibility of going without, you're addicted.

Overcoming food addiction is not the same as overcoming alcoholism or drug abuse. People who want to overcome these addictions know they can't use them or be anywhere they are prominent. For example, people who want to stop drinking alcohol should never frequent a bar, tavern, or pub. The temptation is too great. But you must eat and you want food that tastes good. Most people who go on diets fail because they don't eat enough or don't eat enough of the right foods.

Options for Overcoming Food Addictions

You can use the "all or nothing" approach if you have the willpower to stop cold turkey. Most people get the nothing part because this approach is too drastic for them and their cravings for unhealthy food is too intense. Alternatively, you could eliminate one unhealthy food until your addiction to that food has subsided and then tackle another one.

I did that many years ago. I started with coffee. Once my addiction to coffee subsided (I went through serious withdrawal), I moved on to soda. I didn't experience the same physical withdrawal symptoms I did with coffee, but my cravings for soda lasted much, much longer. Finally, I gave up junk food and eating at fast food restaurants. The entire process took about six months. Now, I have coffee occasionally, but no soft drinks or junk food, and rarely eat at fast food restaurants.

Moving Forward

You are now armed with all the information necessary to successfully prevent or recover from the emotional pain of depression. The final key that will ensure your success is preparation. Knowing what to do when will help you adhere to the changes in your life that provide emotional freedom. As Benjamin Franklin is attributed to saying, *"By failing to prepare, you are preparing to fail."*

Summary

• Many daily behaviors and habits contribute to the development of or worsen depression.

• While these behaviors and habits may not directly trigger depression, they contribute to the effects of stress and anxiety that lead to depression.

• The factors we considered included sleep, physical activity, and diet. There are numerous other behaviors that contribute to poor mental and physical health. You can learn more about these behaviors in my book, *Stressed to Success: Upgrading Your Life*.

WOLFMIND

STRONGER IN THE PACK

Chapter 6
Creating an Action Plan for Success

Before helping you develop your Action Plan, one final thought must be considered; the role of willpower in adhering to that plan. Most people try to force themselves to succeed. Unfortunately, willpower rarely works. Willpower is in the realm of the conscious mind. However, humans tend to use their conscious mind only five percent of the time.

According to Dr. Bruce Lipton, the other 95% of the time, we react to life unconsciously. He further states that this makes our subconscious a million times more powerful than our conscious mind, so it can hijack our efforts to use willpower to change. Just ask anyone who has ever tried to quit smoking, diet, or start an exercise program.

Knowing that willpower rarely works improves your chances for success by taking that fact into account when creating and attempting to adhere to your Action Plan. If you find yourself sliding back – STOP – use SADAR to keep your subconscious from hijacking your desires, making sure you add your affirmations for self-love and gratitude. Once you verbalize your power, using the He-Man technique, your subconscious power fades, providing you with the courage to continue. Be sure to include SADAR as part of your Action Plan.

To be successful, your Action Plan must contain the following elements;

- An understanding and acknowledgment of the sources of your depression
- The effects that runaway fight-or-flight reflexes and Negative Programming Cycles exert on your experience of life

- The ability to intervene to stop your fight-or-flight and Negative Programming Cycle from taking over your life
- The ability to use the human superpower, neuroplasticity, to rewire your brain for happiness and success and to overcome the destructive effects of dysfunctional memories
- Upgrading your life to eliminate those factors that contribute to or worsen your stress, anxiety, and depression
- Creating an Action Plan to succeed

Risk Factors for Depression

Depression is a complex disease that may be caused by one or more of the following factors, including genetics, biology, social and personal problems, medication, and diet. Please check all that may apply to your situation and answer the questions relating to each of those factors.

_____ Genetics: Who in my family suffers from depression?

_____ Biology (You may not be able to answer this question.)

_____ Physical, emotional, or sexual abuse

_____ Personal conflicts (home, work, school, other)

_____ Loss or death of loved one

_____ Caring for someone experiencing the grief of a lost loved one

_____ Experience or exposure to violence

_____ New job

_____ Graduating from high school, college, or other institution of higher learning

_____ Recently married

_____ Birth of a child

_____ Move to a new house, state, or country

Loss of job or income _____

Divorce _____

Recently retired _____

Serious illness or injury reducing quality of life _____

Substance abuse (alcohol, illicit or prescriptive drugs) _____

Diet _____

Side effects of any medications you're taking _____

Other, not listed here _____

All these factors increase your risk for developing depression. The more you list, the greater your chances of falling victim to this disabling disease. The more intense or longer you have been exposed, the greater your risk.

Effects of Conditioning

Genetics may play less of a role in the development of depression than originally thought. Your risk of depression may be more the result of exposure to family members suffering from depression or reacting emotionally to unwanted or aversive life experiences. Remember, human behaviors are more the result of conditioning than they are from genetics. Early life caretakers, like parents and grandparents, condition us on three levels, deliberately, deliberately but with unintentional consequences, and accidentally.

Most, if not all our dysfunctional reactions to unwanted or aversive life situations are the result of deliberate training with unintended consequences or accidentally through the modeling of dysfunctional reactions. Being aware of others dysfunctional reactions can prompt you to make choices that immunize you from their dysfunction. Below, check all individuals or societal institutions that trigger your dysfunctional emotional reactions to unwanted or aversive experiences.

_____ Parents

_____ Siblings

_____ Grandparents

_____ Other family members

_____ Friends

_____ Classmates

_____ Coworkers

_____ Television

_____ Radio

_____ Social Media

_____ Others Not Listed Here

Review your social contacts to determine who affects your mental and emotional state at any given time. In some cases, it may be necessary to remove these people or influences from your life. In many cases, that will not be an option. You will then need to use SADAR to mitigate their effects, so you gain emotional freedom from their influence.

Situations Perceived as Stressful

_____ Home

_____ School

_____ Work

_____ Sports

Other (List)   _____

Other (List)   _____

Other (List)   _____

Other (List)   _____

Other (List)   _____

How often do you worry about distressful situations? _____

With 10 being completely stressed, how stressed do you get? _____

What happens to you when you get stressed?

Inability to control thoughts _____

Can't think _____

Inability to control emotions _____

Worry _____

Loss of memory _____

Loss of ability to focus _____

Loss of ability to problem-solve _____

Negative thoughts about myself, others, the world _____

Feelings of helplessness and hopelessness _____

Feelings of incompetence _____

Desire to give up or withdraw from the situation _____

Conflict with others _____

Blurred vision _____

Tense or jittery muscles (butterflies in stomach) _____

Joint or muscle pain _____

Rapid, shallow breathing or holding your breath _____

Sadness or depression _____

Anger _____

Frustration _____

Other (List) _____

Other (List) _____

Now you know when you are affected by life and how that manifests itself. These are reminders to use SADAR to intervene in the fight-or-flight reflex and Negative Programming Cycles that define your experience in unwanted or aversive situations. Remember, these are normal reactions to fear and your perceptions of threat to how you want life to treat you. They only cause problems when they control your life and overwhelm your ability to control your internal reality.

Use of Methods to Overcome Fight-or-Flight Reflex and Negative Programming Cycles

The more you use SADAR and the techniques for rewiring your brain for happiness and success, the faster and more complete your recovery from stress, anxiety, and depression. Below, list when, how often, and how you intend on using these methods.

Method	Morning	Night	# times during the day	How long? (Minutes)	Daily	Weekly
SADAR	___	___	___	___	___	___
Meditation (Happiness)	___	___	___	___	___	___
Meditation (Success)	___	___	___	___	___	___
Mediation (Self-esteem)	___	___	___	___	___	___
Meditation (Gratitude)	___	___	___	___	___	___
Meditation (Memories)	___	___	___	___	___	___

For best results, it will be necessary to use SADAR at least 10-20 times a day for 30 consecutive days. After that, performing it 2-3 times a week; morning and night may be all that's necessary to help you remember to use it when you need it. Of course, it will be even more effective if you make it a lifetime habit, especially if your life is marked by a lot of stress and anxiety or you are already in a state of depression.

Because of space limitations, the term "Meditation" is used to describe the Visualization/Imagery exercises that get your imagination to work for you where it may have worked against you in the past. The more you have control over your imagination, the less risk for depression you will experience or the faster your recovery from depression if you're already experiencing the emotional pain of not feeling good enough about yourself. Several different intentions have been identified for the use of meditation.

You can use this form of Mental Rehearsal or Visualization/ Imagery to increase your belief in the success and happiness you deserve, to improve your self-love or self-esteem, to remove your self-consciousness by directing your attention to those things in life for which you are grateful, or to replace memories of failure or unhappiness, so they don't invade your thoughts in the future.

Lifestyle Upgrades

In Chapter 6, you were exposed to three lifestyle habits that contribute to or worsen your experiences of stress, anxiety, and depression. Your adherence to any changes you desire will be greatly increased if you write out which aspects of your life you wish to upgrade and then review them regularly. The same thing is true for any of the other behaviors you hope to add or change, like SADAR and Meditation.

Sleep

Right now, I only get _____ continuous hours of sleep daily because I have chosen to do so or because other lifestyle choices interfere. My goal is to increase the amount of time I sleep daily to _____ hours. To help me sleep better I will alter the foods I eat at night_____, remove my smartphone from my bedroom, or stop watching television or listening to the radio _____ at least 1-2 hours before bedtime.

Diet

I will remove the following foods from my diet because they are unhealthy. Please list all that you hope to eliminate and the time frame for their elimination. List the order you wish to eliminate them. You may not want to try and eliminate all unhealthy food choices at the same time, but eliminate one at a time until your addiction to them has died. Take the same approach for foods that you want to include in your diet that you presently don't eat.

Foods to Eliminate

Food	Time Frame
_____	_____
_____	_____
_____	_____
_____	_____

Foods to Include

Food	Time Frame
_____	_____
_____	_____
_____	_____
_____	_____

Physical Activity and Exercise

Sedentary lifestyles contribute to depression. A sedentary lifestyle can be the result of choice, fatigue experienced from stress, anxiety, and depression, or time. Regardless of the cause, physical activity and exercise accelerates your recovery from depression or prevents you from becoming depressed in the first place. You don't need to go to the gym to increase your level of physical activity. Simply standing up at regular intervals during the day or walking for short periods are beneficial to your mental and physical health. If you have not been physically active for some time, please see a physician to determine if it's in your best interest.

I intend on increasing my level of physical activity by making the following adaptations in my daily routine.

_____

_____

_____

_____

_____

_____

_____

_____

You have now been exposed to six important keys that will prevent your descent into or accelerate your recovery from depression. If you are presently under a doctor's orders and taking prescribed medication or in therapy, please do not stop. This book is intended to complement the treatments you are now receiving.

There are many other actions you can take to help aid in your recovery from this unnecessary and debilitating disease. You can find more ways to empower your life in my three-book series, *Stressed to Success: Information, Tools, and Training, Upgrading Your Life, and Workbook and Journal.* They can be found by visiting www. thepeaksolution.com. I wish you well on your journey to mental health.

Works Cited

Breathnach, Sarah Ban. The Simple Abundance: Journal of Gratitude. New York: Warner, 1996. Print.

Csikszentmihalyi, Mihaly. *Flow: The Psychology of Optimal Experience.* New York: Harper Perennial Modern Classics, 1990. Print.

Emmons, Robert, PhD. *Thanks: How Practicing Gratitude Can Make You Happier.* New York: Houghton Mifflin, 2008. Print.

Gladwell, Malcolm. *Outliers: The Story of Success.* New York: Back Bay Books, 2011. Print.

Hanson, Rick, PhD. *Hardwiring Happiness: The New Brain Science of Contentment, Calm, and Confidence.* New York: Harmony Books, 2013. Print.

Helmstetter, Shad, PhD. *What to Say When You Talk to Yourself.* New York: Simon & Schuster, 1982. Print.

Kunduz, David. *Quiet Mind: One-Minute Retreats from a Busy World.* Canada: Comair Press, 2000. Print.

Levine, James, A., PhD, MD. *Get Up! Why Your Chair is Killing You and What You Can Do About It.* New York: St. Martin's Press, 2014. Print.

Lindlahr, Victor H. *You are What You Eat: How to Win and Eat Health with Diet.* New York: National Nutrition Society, Inc., 1942. Print.

Lipton, Bruce H., PhD. *The Biology of Belief: Unleashing the Power of Consciousness, Matter & Miracles.* Carlsbad: Hay House, Inc., 2008. Print.

Oechsli, Matt. *Winning the Inner Game of Selling.* Greensboro: The Oechsli Institute, 1990. Print.

Sapolsky, Robert M. *Why Zebras Don't Get Ulcers.* New York: Holt Paperbacks, 2004. Print.

Siegel, Daniel J. *The Mindful Brain: Reflection and Attunement in the Cultivation of Well-being.* New York: W. W. Norton & Company, Inc., 2007. Print.

Other Books by Dr. Piparo

- *Stressed to Success: Information, Tools, and Training*
- *Stressed to Success: Upgrading Your Life*
- *Stressed to Success: Workbook and Journal*
- *Stressed to Success: Freedom from Test Anxiety*
- *Kingdom of the Tiger: A Golfer's Guide to Playing in The Zone*
- *Target Oriented Golf: Training the Eyes and Mind for Success*
- *Ascent into Hell*
- *Freedom from Test Anxiety*

The above books are available from:

The Peak

(414) 366-0469

Tony@ThePeakSolution.com

www.ThePeakSolution.com

About the Author

Dr. Tony Piparo is a Performance Psychologist and author of such books as *Stressed to Success: Information, Tools, and Training, Stressed to Success: Upgrading Your Life, Stressed to Success: Workbook and Journal, Kingdom of the Tiger: A Golfer's Guide to Playing in The Zone, Target Oriented Golf: Training the Eyes, Mind, and Body for Success, Freedom from Test Anxiety, and Ascent into Hell*. His books have been an inspiration and help to thousands of people worldwide.

His academic training includes a Bachelor's in Education, a Masters in Curriculum and Instruction, specializing in Learning Theory, a second Masters in Kinesiology (the study of human movement and exercise), and a PhD in Performance Psychology. As he will tell you, his real education started after completing his academic career. His quest for answers to his life-long struggles with stress, anxiety, and depression led him on a journey on which he met amazing specialists from a variety of fields, whose insight and wisdom helped him understand why he suffered from these destructive conditions and to alternative treatments that eliminated his emotional pain.

Dr. Piparo believes that you have the power to end your suffering. You have the power to control your life. You have the power to eliminate your emotional pain and improve your health and performance in every aspect of your life. You have the power to alter your brain's structure, chemistry, and function. You even have the power to alter your DNA and gene expression. By understanding what causes your emotional pain and depression and taking the appropriate steps, you have the power to experience happiness and success where you may have been plagued with sadness and failure in the past. You will live more successfully, productively, and abundantly with greater happiness, joy, love, and prosperity.

YES, YOU ARE THAT POWERFUL!

Let Dr. Piparo show you how.

Contact Dr. Tony Piparo

(414) 366-0469

Tony@ThePeakSolution.com

www.ThePeakSolution.com

www.FreedomFromDepression.org

CPSIA information can be obtained
at www.ICGtesting.com
Printed in the USA
FFHW011813100219
50462471-55693FF

9 780976 967675